D1083190

Books by

Anauta and Heluiz Washburne

LAND OF THE GOOD SHADOWS
The Life Story of an Eskimo Woman

CHILDREN OF THE BLIZZARD

by Anauta

The John Day Company

Wild like the Foxes

The true story of an Eskimo Girl

ew York

 Published by The John Day Company, 62 West 45th Street, New York 36, N.Y., and on the same day in Canada by Longmans, Green & Company, Toronto.

Library of Congress Catalog Card
Number: 56-5975

MANUFACTURED IN THE UNITED STATES OF AMERICA

INTRODUCTION

THE EVENTS in this story I seem to have known always. Bits of it were told to me by my father, Yorgke, when on some stormy winter night I would beg him for a story. Then I would lie in my sleeping bag and ponder long the things I had heard. They always made a deep impression on my ever imaginative childish mind, as I tried to realize that this had really happened in the life of Alea, the gentle, quiet woman who was my mother.

In the book *Land of the Good Shadows* the adult life of Yorgke and Alea lives on. May the readers learn to love them as friends as I loved them as my parents.

Sincerely,

ᐊᓇᐅᑕ

(Anauta)

CONTENTS

WILD LIKE THE FOXES

1

AN INTERRUPTED JOURNEY

A BOAT slowly nosed its way through the calm water until it came to rest on the sand of the shore. Ahpea jumped out and helped his wife, Soona, and two children to land. While he pulled the boat higher up on the shore, the others ran on up the hill and were soon out of sight. Then he walked a short distance, seated himself on a flat rock, and proceeded to light his pipe.

"What a wonderful day this is! What a fine trip," he mused.

The past year had been a good one for the Eskimo hunters and trappers of the Labrador. The winter had been, for the most part, cold and clear. Deer and foxes had been plentiful. In the spring the off-shore winds had helped the Eskimos to secure a good catch of seals and walrus. So, Ahpea had been able to purchase this fine boat and the supplies for next winter that it contained. The skins and furs had been sufficient to pay for all. He felt happy and carefree as he sat there puffing on his pipe.

He smiled as he thought of Koopah. How surprised the boy had been when he handed him the new rifle at the store yesterday saying, "There's your new gun, son. Put it in the boat before you forget it."

The boy had looked at it unbelievingly. At last he asked slowly, "Mine? This is mine?"

On being convinced that it really was his own, Koopah had held it tightly in his hand and, with a quivering face, had looked up at Ahpea and said, "Wait 'til that seal pokes his old head up next time."

Koopah was not Ahpea's own son, but Ahpea loved him as much as if he were. What a weak little fellow he used to be. That was because he was so nearly gone when Ahpea brought him home—a little, undernourished boy, just able to walk.

How well Ahpea remembered the time he had been hunting along the rugged coast late in the fall, believing himself many miles from everyone. He had been startled when he heard a child's faint cry. Following the sound he had walked around a point of land and found a tent. He never forgot the sight that faced him when he opened the flap and peered inside. Even before he entered he knew the parents were dead. Starvation—that was plain. But the little boy had strangely survived.

Ahpea had wrapped his coat around the little boy and carried him home. Soona had nursed him and learned to love him as her own. They learned from his lisping words that his name was Koopah. He was fourteen now, a sturdy lad and a good hunter. For some time, he had needed a new rifle and Ahpea felt glad that at last he was able to give him one. The boy would do well with it next winter.

Ahpea heard Soona and the children laughing. Evidently they were after partridges. "They must be throwing stones at them, for the guns are in the boat," he thought.

When it came to fun, Soona was as full of it as any child. She had laughing eyes, dark and shining. Her face was animated and full of expression. She was an ideal companion for Ahpea, who was, himself, a quiet man. He had always found her resourceful at times when resourcefulness was needed. Yes, he was a happy man with his wife, Soona, his daughter, Alea, and Koopah. If only next year would be as good, he was thinking, when Soona's shout far up the hill made him glance toward the shore.

"The boat! The boat!"

He jumped up and ran for the water. The boat was drifting away. A light wind had sprung up and the rising tide had floated it off. Ahpea waded out up to his waist, but being unable to swim, he feared to lunge forward. He tried several times but the boat was beyond his reach. Slowly he walked back to the shore.

Soona, Alea and Koopah stared at the boat going farther and farther away. No one spoke. The water from Ahpea's clothes made puddles in the sand about his feet. Silently, the family watched their boat, their clothes and supplies, their guns and ammunition, everything, drifting out to sea.

A sudden movement from Soona broke the tension. She would get the boat! Quickly she ran to a fallen tree that was washing up and down in the waves on the beach. This she pushed out into deeper water. It was so sodden from having been in the sea a long time that only half of it floated above the surface. Her face was bright with love for her family and her determination to help them. No situation had ever been too difficult for her. She was used to acting quickly, so now she turned to them with her usual happy smile and said, "Soona will get the boat. Wait here until I return. I won't be gone long. Wait."

Ahpea saw what she intended to do. She would float out on that log already deep in the water and try to reach the boat.

"No, no, Soona. You must not go on that. It will not hold you. You will not be able to guide it," he said earnestly.

But she answered, "The wind will blow me to the boat. You stay here with Koopah and Alea. I will hurry."

She turned to the little girl and boy who were watching their mother working with the log and said, "Be a good girl, Alea. Anana, your mother, will get the boat. Koopah, take care of Alea until I get back."

Ahpea caught hold of the end of the log as Soona seated herself upon it. "Soona, you must not go out. It will not do. The log will not hold you. Never mind the boat now. We have always found a way. You must not go," he pleaded.

But Soona only smiled at him over her shoulder and answered, "I will be all right. I must get the boat. The tide and the wind will drive me to it."

It was madness. Ahpea felt sick. Soona could not possibly hold on with her legs dangling in the water. She would be chilled after a while. He watched her start to drift away, paddling with a short stick. He could not let her go alone. If he could not stop her from going, then he must go too. Picking up a long stick he ran out, caught up with her and sat on the log behind her. His weight made the log sink deeply in the water.

"You must not come, Ahpea," Soona said earnestly. "No need for both of us to go."

"I can't let you go alone. Let us go back," Ahpea pleaded. "We must not leave Alea and Koopah alone."

"No, Ahpea, we must get the boat," replied Soona. "Our guns, our clothes for next winter, everything we have are in it. Alea and Koopah will be safe."

She was leaning forward with her hands on the log in front of her. "See, we are drifting in the same direction as the boat. We will get it all right."

He felt it was a hopeless thing they were doing but he could not stop Soona. He hoped the water would not get too rough. Even now the log was rolling uncomfortably. He looked for the boat and saw it far out, drifting ever farther away.

There was a branch between them and Ahpea was able to hold to this for support. "Can you lean against the branch, Soona?" he asked.

Soona did not answer but leaned back until she could touch it. She soon tired of the upright position, however, and leaned forward again.

"That makes me tired. It's better this way," she said.

They were not paddling now—just drifting with the tide. For a long time they were silent. There seemed nothing to say. The only sound was the water lapping against the log. So, the hours went by while they drifted slowly far out to sea.

2

LONELY HOURS

BACK ON THE SHORE, the boy and girl watched their parents floating away on the log. From the ever-widening distance, the man and woman looked as though they were sitting in the water. Before long, they vanished from sight.

Alea began to cry. She was only ten years old. Koopah did not speak. So much had happened in so short a time that he felt bewildered. And he realized the danger their parents were facing. Suppose they didn't catch up with the boat? How would they get back? Ahpea and Soona couldn't possibly paddle against the wind. And here he was with Alea alone on this island with nothing but what they had on.

Koopah seemed older than his fourteen years. He was an Eskimo boy who had been taught to act quickly. He had often faced difficult situations and learned to do what seemed to be best under the circumstances. So with a long, last look he turned to his sobbing sister.

Quietly looking down at her, he said teasingly, "Alea looks nice, all but her face. That has water that runs from two holes that look like the setting sun. I do not care for it so. If the waters streaming from those two holes would cease flowing, we could go and see if we could find more birds."

His sister wiped her eyes on her sleeve and answered with a sob, "But when will they come back?"

He planted his legs far apart and looked solemnly at his sad companion. "My sister asks me a silly question. When will they come back? I don't answer because I know they'll come as soon as they can. Now, little Alea, no more water!"

This made Alea smile. Koopah knew how to cheer her. They were pals. He himself had never been able to remember his parents who had died. Ahpea and Soona were his parents and this was his sister. He loved her dearly. Although they both knew Koopah's story, it made no difference to them. Koopah was Alea's idol and his teasing was typical of his fun-loving nature. At times he would torment her into a temper and the more angry she became the more fun he had. But they understood each other and he would protect her with his life if necessary.

They spent the afternoon walking around the small, rocky island. Late in the evening they climbed to the highest point and gazed far out to sea. There was no sign of the boat nor of the two on the log. As the night shadows closed in, Koopah and Alea sat quietly near the shore. Except for the noise of the wind, which was quite strong now, and the waves that washed up and down against the rocks, there was no sound.

The air was getting sharper. Alea shivered, "I'm cold," she declared.

Koopah jumped up. "Come on, let us get dry sticks and make a fire."

There were no trees on the island but plenty of driftwood had washed onto the shore. Soon they had gathered a large pile of wood. Then they rolled away the larger rocks and cleared a fireplace. Koopah took a piece of flint and part of a file from his pocket. He struck the flint against the steel and made the sparks fly. As the sparks dropped on the dry moss, it began to smoke. Koopah puffed and blew until a bright blaze sprang up. Adding small, dry twigs, he soon had a good fire started and Alea put larger sticks on it. Clearing away more rocks by the fire, they made a comfortable place to sit.

The warmth of the fire felt good, but soon Alea had another complaint. "I'm hungry."

Koopah sat still for a while; then he jumped up so suddenly he nearly knocked Alea over backward.

"Where are the birds?" he shouted.

"What birds?" Alea asked, wondering what he was so excited about.

"The birds we killed with rocks today," he answered.

Now it was her turn to jump up. It was she who had been carrying the birds when her mother first saw the boat drifting away and started running toward the shore. Alea had dropped the birds as she swiftly followed her mother.

Now she said to Koopah, "I dropped them by that rock. Come on, they're still up there. It's dark but I know where to find them, somewhere near that rock yonder."

They searched in all directions, feeling around with their hands. At last, Alea found the birds and the two carried them back to the fireplace.

In the minds of both was the memory of the morning's events. They had found those partridges over on the other side of the island. That was what Soona had laughed so much about, when Ahpea heard her as he sat on the rock. She had thrown a rock at one of the birds, missed it, and hit one that she had not seen until it bounced up and fell over dead. That was funny, killing a bird without knowing it was there. Then Koopah had got the other one.

Back beside their fire, Koopah tried to pluck the birds but the feathers did not come out easily, so he pulled the skin off. After he had cleaned and washed the partridges in the sea water, brother and sister each put one on a long stick and began the slow process of cooking it over the fire. The smell of roasting made them so hungry they could hardly wait for the birds to be done. When at last the partridges were cooked, Alea and Koopah picked every bone clean. Nothing was wasted.

Then Alea began to grow sleepy.

"Tell me about Big Star Hunter," she said, looking up at the clear sky with its thousands of bright stars.

Koopah, too, looked up at the night sky. Since the time he was Alea's age, he had made imaginary people out of the stars, telling stories about them. Alea loved to listen, so now he began.

"The stars are people. The dull, small ones are those who never do very much. The big bright ones are the ones who do big things. See that one over there. That is

Big Star Hunter. He is the brightest of them all. He shines brightest and biggest because he is not afraid of anything. He is not afraid of the other stars nor even the moon. I expect today he outran all the others. He knows no fear. It is because of the fire that burns within him. He is all goodness and happiness. See, Alea, the moon is laughing at him, but Big Star Hunter just blinks his eyes and smiles in return. When I'm a man, I want to be just like Big Star Hunter."

"Why is Big Star Hunter not afraid of the other stars? There are so many of them and he is only one," Alea asked wonderingly.

"Big Star Hunter is sorry the others do not try harder to be better. If they cared enough they could be bright too, but they are the lazy ones. They are satisfied as they are." And Koopah nodded his head wisely.

Soon Alea was asleep. Koopah laid her head on his lap and before long he, too, was dozing. Now and then he awoke to put more sticks on the fire. The night was cold and Alea cuddled up until her knees nearly touched her chin. Koopah took off his coat, put it over her and held her closely, trying to give her of his warmth.

With the first light of dawn he gently laid Alea on the ground, added more wood to the fire, then leaned close to the flames to warm himself. He felt sore and stiff from sitting so long in his cramped position, but he had not wanted to disturb Alea's sleep.

When Alea awoke, she sat up just in time to see Koopah race down the hill, jumping in great leaps and blowing on his fingers. He looked wild with his black hair all moppy and disheveled. When he saw her sitting up, he raced back, coming to a breathless stop in front of her.

"I never heard anyone snore like Alea. Just like an old mother seal," he teased.

"I don't snore. You do," she contradicted.

"You did snore. I thought it was two mother seals. I was wishing I had my new rifle—" he stopped short. His rifle was in the boat. Where was the boat now and the two on the log? Would this day bring them back?

Alea's eyes anxiously searched the water. But she did not speak.

Then Koopah said lightly, "Come on and get warmed up. We will look for more birds."

That day they killed three more birds with stones and roasted them as they had done the day before. They spent the rest of the day watching and waiting. Sometimes they climbed to the top of their lookout and searched the sea for the boat, but there was nothing. At last it grew dark again and further watching was useless. So they again sat by their fire, silent and anxious. At first Koopah tried to keep up a carefree conversation, but at last he, too, stared silently into the embers of the fire.

Long after Alea was asleep he sat wondering what they should do. In all his life Koopah had never felt so lonely as he did then. The hours of the night went by slowly. He wished he could sleep, but he was too anxious and worried and sleep did not come.

3

TRAGEDY

THE WATER washed gently up and down the shore, making a swishing sound that lulled the senses of the man lying on the sand. Slowly he opened his eyes, then closed them again. The sun blinded him and he was very weary. He was dimly conscious that his body was on the sand and that his legs were being moved by the waves. He lay inert, trying to remember. Memory was slow in coming. He tried to sit up, but fell back again. Slowly it came to him about the log that rolled and tumbled in the darkness. He had clung to the branch. There had been a sudden lurch as the log floated up, relieved of Soona's weight when she fell off.

The man on the beach covered his face with his hands. "Soona," he whispered in anguish. Yes, he had reached out for her desperately.

Once he heard her voice in the darkness. She seemed to be crying, "Alea!"

But that was all—nothing more except the lapping of the waves against the log. He had gone on calling, but there was no answering sound. Ahpea now remembered the long drifting alone with his grief in the blackness of the night, then nothing more until now.

He sat up and looked about him. There was the log being rolled up and down by the waves a short distance away. Laboriously he crawled farther up on the shore. He tried to stand but his knees gave way. He untied his boots and took them off. His feet were numb from being so long in the water. He lay down again and drifted off to sleep.

When Ahpea next awoke, he felt better and was able to stand. He still felt weak as from a long illness. He wondered how he had lived to reach land. Somehow he must have been able to keep his head above water.

Where was he? He wondered how far he was from the island where Koopah and Alea were. He could not return on the log. He would have to go against the wind and the tide to find his way back to where he had started. But first, he must regain his strength. Even now the ground seemed to rise up and down when he tried to walk, so he sat down again. He wondered how long he had been unconscious.

When the dizziness passed, he walked to a high place and looked out toward the horizon. He saw several islands and far beyond them the mainland reached long and blue in the distance. He searched the stretch of nearby shore, thinking the boat might have drifted here too, but there was no sign of it.

He had been long without food and felt hungry. On the hillside he found berries. They were delicious and grew in abundance. He felt better after eating some.

Returning to the shore, he gathered large stout sticks and set to work making a raft. With the aid of a small pocket knife, he cut strips of skin from his sealskin coat and used them to fasten the wood together. His boot strings, too, went into fastenings for his raft. The raft was not very large but it would hold him above water. He next searched the shore for two suitable poles to use as paddles and, finding them, he fastened them in so that he could row with them. Since it was late by the time he finished, he lay down to wait for daylight to make his return trip.

The next morning dawned calm and sunny. Ahpea launched his raft and paddled away. He kept near the shore until he saw the island with the hill in the center. He knew that was where Alea and Koopah must be. Ahpea paddled slowly, dreading the moment when he must tell his sad news. Alea's and Koopah's mother was gone. They would all have to go on now without her. His heart was very heavy.

It was late afternoon when, from their lookout, Koopah saw the movement of the paddle in the sun. Quickly catching hold of Alea's arm, he pointed excitedly.

"Look, Alea! Look out there! Something is moving. See? There it is again!"

They stared out over the water. Yes, a dark object was coming closer. How they danced and laughed in their glee! Their parents were coming at last.

"They are coming! They are coming!" sang Alea.

All the dread and anxiety were over. She was wild with joy.

They looked hard at the approaching object. Soon they could see it was not the boat but Ahpea alone on a raft.

"Anana must be with the boat. Atata, our father, comes alone," Alea said as she ran toward the shore.

Koopah followed more slowly. Fear clutched at his heart. If Ahpea and Soona had found the boat, why did Ahpea come alone?

Alea called, "Where is my Anana?" as the raft ran ashore and Ahpea stood up to come to them.

Ahpea looked at them and said, "I am glad you are all right. I was afraid for you."

Koopah saw his father's tense expression and was silent, waiting to hear more.

Ahpea strove for composure to break the news. Putting his arm about Alea he drew her close as he said, "Your mother was very brave. She tried to get the boat so we would not suffer next winter. She could not hold on when the sea got rough. She called your name, Alea, after she fell off. I think she was saying you were not to cry if she could not come back."

Ahpea's tears were bitter as he broke down and wept. Koopah walked away quietly. He had to be alone. He was too grieved to speak. All he knew now was that their mother was never coming back to them. On the other side of the island he threw himself down and sobbed bitterly until at last he was worn out and fell asleep.

When Ahpea and Alea went looking for Koopah, they found him still sleeping. Ahpea woke him and said, "Son, we have lost everything we had for next winter. We have no guns, food, clothes, or anything, and worst of all, we have no boat. We must get help somehow. What shall we do?"

Koopah sat up. Ahpea was treating him like a man, asking for his advice.

Ahpea continued, "First, we must make a bigger raft and get to the mainland. Then we must go to Aiviktok Trading Post for more supplies if the trader will let us have them when we have no skins to pay for them. If he will not let us have guns and cartridges, son, we will be in a bad way."

Koopah replied quietly, "Let us go now before we starve. I am already hungry."

Ahpea answered with deep concern. "Yes, we must think of that too. Now, let us find wood for our raft."

All evening the three worked, gathering large sticks and tying them firmly together with the strips of skin they took from the other raft. They did not have enough strips for a larger raft, so they decided to make two trips to the mainland.

After they were through working, they walked over the island and managed to get two partridges, which they divided. It was too late to go to the mainland that day, so they rested by their fire, slept as much as they could, and waited for the dawn. When, at last, the sun rose, Ahpea and Koopah decided that Alea should be the first to be taken on the raft to the mainland.

As Ahpea and Alea boarded the raft and pushed off, Ahpea said that he would hurry back to get Koopah and told him not to worry. Koopah waved goodbye and stood in silence, as the raft with its passengers grew small in the distance. Then he threw some wood on the fire.

All day he waited anxiously for his father to return. He watched from the shore until the night closed in and he could no longer look out over the sea. Sitting there alone he gazed upward at the stars. A smile came to his anxious face when he saw Big Star Hunter. Yes, there the Hunter was, as big and bright as ever, looking right down at him. Koopah no longer felt so alone. Lying down beside the fire, he slept peacefully.

The water was calm and the air felt warm as Ahpea paddled the raft to the shore. It was late afternoon when he and Alea got to the mainland and looked about to find a suitable place for Alea to stay while her father went back for Koopah. Together they chose a grassy hollow for the spot where the girl should wait.

"Don't walk into the woods, Alea," Ahpea warned. "And don't go too far away from this place. I don't like leaving you here alone but there is no other way. I will hurry back as soon as I get Koopah."

Alea glanced uneasily toward the forest. "Are there wolves in the woods?" she asked.

"I won't say there are not," her father said, but he smiled reassuringly. "Yes, there are wolves in these parts, but remember they are cowards. I'll build a fire. Keep it going and the coward wolves will stay away. They won't go near a fire. Be of good courage, my daughter. I shall return as soon as possible."

Ahpea's heart was heavy. How small Alea looked, and pale. She had cried so that her face was blotchy. He held her in his arms a moment, then ran down and pushed the raft out into the water for the return trip to the island.

Bravely, Alea watched her father go, waving her hand to show him she was not afraid. She had often been alone before. She had even stayed out all night on hunting trips, but then she had always had her gun and she had been taught early how to use it. Now she had nothing but her hands. Suppose the wolves came? But Alea's keen sense of humor came to her rescue. Well, if the wolves came and ate her up, they would not be hungry any more and she would not be hungry either because she would be inside them. So, they would all feel fine. She chuckled at the amusing thought. And, because it was silly to laugh by herself, she laughed again. Then she turned and walked along the bank to the blueberry bushes she and Ahpea had noticed. She ate all she could, then gathered more for her father and brother. They would be hungry when they came.

Back by the fire, Alea sat thinking of all that had happened since that day when they started home from the trading post. They had been so happy! Now her mother was gone. Alea began to cry in her loneliness. How could she ever live without her mother? Now she needed her more than ever. Putting more wood on the fire, Alea cried herself to sleep.

When Ahpea and Koopah returned, they found Alea still sleeping. When she heard them she jumped up, delighted that they were there. They breakfasted with the berries she had picked for them, then discussed plans for their next step. Ahpea was anxious to waste no time in getting help. He remembered that once before Koopah had been very near death from starvation. Now he might face it again, and Alea and he, too, if they delayed.

"Koopah," he said, "we must get to Aiviktok Post for more supplies. We can't do that without a boat, so I must hunt along the coast and see if I can find some trapper. It's pretty late in the summer. Most of the trappers have gone to their winter hunting grounds far inland, but there might be someone hunting seals along the shore. If I come upon no other trapper, I'll have to go on until I reach the Scotchman Jamieson and his wife. They always remain later than the others. But I hope I need not go that far to find help.

"Alea could not stand the trip. And we must not leave her alone. Also, I can make better time by myself. You, therefore, must remain with Alea. There is no other way. I shall hope it will not be long before I come back to you, my children, with help and food."

The day was cloudy and not so warm as it had been. A chill wind was blowing. Ahpea searched for a more sheltered spot in which to leave his family. Finding one that satisfied him, he fashioned with Koopah's help a crude hut of saplings and piled branches within for beds.

"See what a good house I have for you," he said. "Stay near it, don't go too far away, and all will be well."

"Please let us go with you," Koopah begged hopefully.

But his father answered, "No, son, I will go faster alone."

Ahpea knew the country over which he must travel. It would be bad walking indeed, with mountains and rivers he would have to cross somehow, but their lives depended on his finding help.

A lump rose in his throat as he looked at them standing there, smiling bravely to show him it was all right. They would do as he had bade them. He knew they must both be hungry, just as he was. Berries were not very filling. There was no time to lose if they were to survive. He must hurry!

So he turned and left them, with a prayer in his heart for help in this, their hour of great need.

4

THE TRAPPER'S TENT

AHPEA FOUND THE WAY slow and difficult. As he walked determinedly on, he tried to keep in sight of the shore. He knew that was where trappers would be if any still remained in that vicinity. But the way was rough, with much brush and marshland. Often he had to climb over hills and down the other side to keep from having to go around the cape that jutted far out to sea. This saved him many miles.

All day, stopping only to eat a few berries, he pushed on until it got too dark for him to see. Then he sank down to rest for the night. He had not realized how tired he was. He was very hungry and he knew Koopah and Alea, too, needed food. This was the fifth day since they had lost the boat.

"I must find help. I must! I must!" he said to himself. At last, through sheer exhaustion, he fell asleep.

As soon as dawn began to lighten the sky, Ahpea was on his way, often running downhill. All day he hurried on, searching the water for a boat or a kayak or a tent along the banks near the shore. But save for the gulls, he saw nothing. Once he heard the crashing of a big animal in the woods, but he did not pause. Sometimes he stopped to eat blueberries. The sweet juice quenched his thirst and momentarily relieved the empty feeling in his stomach. But he knew that his people had sometimes died of starvation, even though plenty of blueberries were at hand.

Now his knees began to tremble and he stumbled often, but still he hurried. Another day was coming to an end. Soon it would be too dark to go on. He must rest when he reached the top of the hill he was climbing. He could walk no farther tonight. And he knew he could not stop until he came to the Scotchman and his wife.

Early in the afternoon of the next day, he saw the small tent nestled among the rocks in a sheltered cove far below. Shouting hoarsely, he ran down the hill. The shouts brought the Scotchman and his wife outside.

What they saw amazed them. A man with his clothes ragged and torn, his face gaunt and scratched by branches, running and stumbling toward them. Then the trapper recognized him.

"Ahpea, what's happened to you, mon?" asked the Scotchman in deep concern.

Ahpea was too exhausted to speak immediately and sat breathing hard until he could reply.

"I need help, Jamieson," he gasped. "Koopah and Alea are starving. I must return to them at once with food. I must hurry!"

The Jamiesons helped him into the tent. They saw he was greatly distressed as well as half starved and they asked no questions until Mrs. Jamieson made some hot broth and he had been fed.

They were shocked to hear of Ahpea's loss. At the trading post, they had come to know the little Eskimo woman well and they liked her very much. Tears ran down Mrs. Jamieson's cheeks as she listened to the story. Yes, Soona was like that. She would have tried to get the boat somehow. She would not have thought of danger to herself, poor little happy woman.

As Ahpea told his sad story, Jamieson was already putting aside food and drinking water for the boat, as well as blankets. He was a rugged man who had come from Scotland when he was young and had settled there on the Labrador where his wife joined him. He knew Ahpea to be a good hunter, honest and steady—a quiet man with a ready smile that showed his good nature. They had been friends for many years.

"Ye better stay here, Ahpea, and get some rest. No need for you to come. I'll find the place," Jamieson said.

But Ahpea would not agree to stay behind. "I can rest in the boat," he declared. "Let us hurry!"

The two men started at once, sailing with a light wind along the coast in the moonlight.

Meanwhile, Alea and Koopah wandered along the hillside or down on the rocks of the shore where they looked at the fish and shells in the water. They could see the beautiful salmon swimming lazily along.

"Oh, look at that big one!" Alea exclaimed. "I could get it if I had a long pole." But when she got a stick she found it was impossible to catch any of the fish, for they darted out of reach like a flash and she could not touch them.

So Koopah and Alea ate more berries, yet they were gradually losing strength. As they huddled together in the dark of the night, they wondered where their father was and when he would come back to them. If he did not find even the Scotchman, what would they do?

"I think we are going to be here until we die, Koopah. We will starve before Father comes," Alea's voice came shakily. "I feel weak already."

This thought startled Koopah. It was true. If Ahpea did not come back, they would shortly die of starvation. For six days now all they had eaten were those birds and some berries, and that was not enough to keep them alive. If only he had a gun! There were deer on the hills, he was sure. If he had a spear he could get fish, but he had nothing with which to get any food.

He looked up at the sky and after a moment's silence said, "Alea, look up. Big Star Hunter is very happy tonight. He would not be smiling like that if we were going to die. I think he is telling us not to be afraid. He seems to be saying, 'You two down there, don't be silly.' He winks his eyes and says, 'Do something. Don't sit there and starve. Do something now. If you try hard enough, you will find something to eat.'"

Just then there was a rustle and stir in the brush close by. Alea was startled.

Koopah said, "It's only a rabbit."

Then he jumped to his feet so suddenly that he knocked

Alea backward, flat on her back. Raising his face to the sky, he said, "Thank you, Big Star Hunter, I'll do as you said."

As Alea picked herself up, she saw Koopah rush off into the woods, stoop down and start to dig in the earth with his fingers. He was working furiously. Had he lost his mind? Creeping behind a big rock, she peered over the top to see what he would do next. She was further alarmed to see him frantically pulling up long slim roots. She was sure now that he had gone mad and she was terribly frightened. She even thought of running off into the woods, but the wolves were there.

When Koopah returned to his fireplace seat and found her missing, he called, "Alea! Alea, where are you?"

Not getting an answer, he searched frantically for her and stumbled over her as she crouched behind the rock.

"What are you doing there?" he demanded.

"Are you all right? Didn't you lose your mind?" she asked timidly.

"Lose my mind?" he bellowed.

"You were digging in the ground with your fingers and there was nothing to dig for. You knocked me down and said, 'Thank you, Big Star Hunter,' and he didn't give you anything. I thought your mind was gone because your stomach was so empty, like old Koomak. He got tired of being empty and jumped into the sea, but the people pulled him out and he just got wet and cold."

Long before she finished, Koopah had begun to chuckle. Now he laughed heartily. "So I'm crazy! I've got no sense. Just like old Koomak. My sister tells me I'm like old Koomak, who once told Ahpea a big bear chased him and when Ahpea went looking for the bear, all he found were the tracks of Koomak running one way and the tracks of a rabbit running in the other direction. Oh, what a big bear that was!"

Koopah laughed so much he had to lean against the rock to keep from falling down as he remembered that old joke about this no-account man. He took Alea's arm and together they went back to their shelter.

Koopah nodded his head confidently. "Now, go to sleep. I will show you tomorrow what I was digging for."

They had not been sleeping long when a crashing sound in the woods awakened them. What was that? Alea rubbed her eyes and Koopah leaped up and rushed off toward the sound.

Soon he was back with a dead rabbit and said triumphantly, "See, Alea, we are not going to starve. I caught this in the snare I set last night and we will get more!"

Deftly he tore off the skin and without waiting to cook the rabbit, they ate ravenously. The meat was good and strengthening.

"Did Big Star Hunter tell you to get the rabbit?" Alea asked.

"Big Star Hunter said, 'Do something,' and when I heard that noise in the brush, I remembered I knew how to set a snare to catch rabbits. I caught a lot of them like that last winter, so I ran into the woods to find the long thin roots for my snare. I tied one end to that tree and made a slip noose that hung close to the ground, so the rabbit would run right into it and get hung up. I said,

'Thank you' to Big Star Hunter because he made me think of it. He is always wise. And you thought I had lost my mind! If I was not so sleepy I'd chew you up . . . G-r-r-r."

Koopah spread imaginary claws and bared his teeth as he let out vicious growls at Alea, who laughed as she threw handfuls of gravel at him.

It was early morning when they were awakened by the welcome sound of the boat. Koopah and Alea were grateful to see the Scotchman with their father and no time was wasted in getting aboard the boat and pushing off for the return trip. At the tent, Mrs. Jamieson took charge, feeding them with strength-giving deer meat stew. Before long she was busy mending their clothes.

After two days' rest, Jamieson and Ahpea left Alea and Koopah with Mrs. Jamieson and started out for Aiviktok Trading Post. As the two men approached the post a number of people gathered on the shore to see who could be coming in to trade this late in the fall. Most of the trappers had already been there and gone on to their winter hunting grounds. Only those few who now watched the newcomers had not yet returned to their winter homes.

The trading post was a pretty place with its two white wooden buildings built on a smooth, flat grassy meadow. Back of the houses was a mountain of gray rock, towering high up as if to form a majestic background for this quiet place. The foreground stretched down to the sandy shore where the boat was now landing.

"Hello, Ahpea. Hello, Jamieson," called the trader. "What brings you back? I wasn't expecting you until next spring." As the men stepped heavily out of the boat, all those on shore sensed that something was wrong and waited for Ahpea and Jamieson to speak.

Ahpea said, "Mr. Wilson, I've lost everything I had . . . my boat, guns, food, and, worst of all, my wife, too."

As he went on to tell of the tragic accident, the small crowd fell silent. Soona was known to them all. She was kin to some of them. As soon as they could speak, there were exclamations of shock and sympathy and there was deep grief. Soona, always so happy and laughing. They could scarcely believe this thing they heard.

The trader put his hand on Ahpea's shoulder and said, "Ahpea, I am very sorry to hear of your great loss. Your wife was a fine little woman. To the three of you who are left, I shall gladly give all that you need. All, that is, except a boat. I do not have a boat, I grieve to say."

At this, Jamieson said, "You may have this boat of mine, Ahpea. I am going to build a bigger one, come spring. And I won't need two boats then, or one this winter, for that matter."

Ahpea said, "I'll take it and I am grateful. Next year I will pay whatever you say, if hunting is good."

So Ahpea was outfitted at the store, with guns for himself and Koopah, with a smaller gun for Alea, with clothes, traps for foxes, and food and blankets.

"I hope next winter will be a good one," Ahpea said anxiously, as he looked at the supplies. "I shall need a lot of skins to pay for all this."

"You have a fine boy to help you, Ahpea," the trader said with a smile. "I like that boy of yours. He's got a sparkle in his eyes that does one good to see. He'll make a good trapper."

Ahpea felt proud of this praise for Koopah and said, "He is a good boy and already a good hunter."

Ahpea was ready now for the winter and was anxious to get to his hunting place. Next day he left with Jamieson to get Alea and Koopah and return to his home up the bay.

5

THE HOME UP THE BAY

THE EVENING of the day the men reached the tent, Mrs. Jamieson watched Alea running her hand along the length of her new gun's shiny barrel. Mrs. Jamieson could herself use a gun as well as any man, but preferred to attend to her work in the home and let her husband do the hunting. She had no children and her heart went out in sympathy to this girl who had so recently lost her mother. She wished she could go on caring for the sweet wee person, that she could help her in their home.

A little hesitantly, Mrs. Jamieson expressed her thoughts to Ahpea. "I wish you'd leave the lass with me, Ahpea," she began. "She needs a woman's care. She'll be lonesome up the bay with just you and the boy. She needs a mother. I'd like it right well if you would leave her with me instead of taking her with you tomorrow, to your winter place up the bay."

Ahpea glanced at Alea. Although Alea could not speak much English, he knew she understood what Mrs. Jamieson said, for now her knuckles showed white as she tensely held her gun. Her dark eyes were on his face. Ahpea was sure his daughter would not want to be left behind. But was not Mrs. Jamieson's offer a wise one? Would not Alea be better off with a woman's care? There would be days and nights when she would be all alone while Koopah and he were on hunting trips. Mrs. Jamieson was a fine woman. She would be good for Alea.

Ahpea answered slowly, thoughtfully. "Yes, it will be lonely for her up the bay, just as you say. She will miss her mother. She can stay here if she wishes." And he spoke at length to Alea, in their native tongue.

When he had finished, Alea burst out in indignation. "No! No! I want to be with you. I want to go home up the bay with you and Koopah. I won't be any trouble. I can sew and make boots. Anana showed me how. I won't be in the way. Don't leave me!"

Ahpea took her in his arms, saying soothingly, "You have never been in the way, Alea. It is not that. It is just that you will often be alone when Koopah and I are hunting, and it is not good to be alone so much. You will need more help than we can give you."

Koopah looked from one to the other. He felt distressed. He remembered the last thing Soona had said to him. "Take care of Alea."

Now he spoke earnestly to his father. "Anana said for me to take care of Alea. How can I take care of her if she is not with us?"

Ahpea put his pipe in his mouth and turned slowly to Mrs. Jamieson. "You are good to offer Alea your home," he said, "but we must stay together. You see, we belong together. Alea is a good trapper. She began early. She will be a great help to us and we can't do without her."

"Aye, you are a good mon, Ahpea," replied Mrs. Jamieson warmly. "I understand you. But if later you should change your mind, this home will be waiting to welcome her."

So it was settled that Alea would leave with her father and brother when they went away in the morning. But they did not go the next day. It was stormy, with a heavy rain mixed with snow. Ahpea was worried. Sleet already? They must hurry along. Winter might be on them before they were ready for it. They had much to do.

It was three days before they could load the boat with their belongings and start on their journey up the bay.

Mrs. Jamieson was full of motherly concern for Alea, and warned her to be constantly careful. "Don't fall into the cracks in the ice or tumble down the hillside when it gets slippery. Be careful not to get caught out in a blizzard."

The boat was pushed off amid promises to meet next summer. Three days the family journeyed, rowing until their hands were blistered and sore. Sometimes they put up the sail, but there was no breeze in the calm after the storm, so wearily they took up the oars and began rowing again.

It was with thankfulness that at last they rounded the cape and came in sight of their home. There it was, looking still and quiet on the flat, grassy spot, that seemed all the more peaceful because of the ruggedness of the land sursounding it. Alea at the helm steered the boat to a clearing and ran it up on the sand. They got out and together walked silently toward the house. No one felt like talking.

There was no lock on the door. Ahpea pulled the string that lifted the latch and they entered their home. Ahpea had built this house, had even chopped down the trees from which it was made. The logs were round and rough. The cracks were packed with turf and clay. There were two rooms in the house. The floors were covered with clean white sand except that of the inner room, which was covered with many beautiful rugs. In this inner room, which was Soona's and Ahpea's, was the skin of the bear that Ahpea had killed last winter. Soona had been so pleased to have that skin for their own room. The sand on the floor of the outer room had always been kept fresh and clean. It grated under the feet of the three now looking over their home as they moved about.

There were the pretty print curtains at all the windows. Soona had bought the material last summer when they sold their furs to the traders. When Alea saw her mother's clothes folded neatly on the shelf, she began to cry. Koopah was leaning against the wall dejectedly, looking out the window without seeing anything.

Ahpea cleared his throat. "If Soona were here she would not be happy to have us grieve," he said. "I think your mother is right here with us. We can't see her, but she knows all we are doing. Let her see us happy. Come, we must unload the boat."

The thought that her mother was near them was comforting to Alea. And she eagerly followed the others down to the boat to help carry their belongings into the house.

As she hurried toward the shore, Alea wondered if there would be any muskrats at the brook that ran down the hillside a short distance away. There had often been some there, but it was probably still too early. They would not be prime until after the snow came.

The boat's contents were soon safely in the house, and the boat itself was pulled up on land, turned bottom up and weighted down with heavy rocks to keep it safe from sudden storms.

The fine day was coming to a glorious sunset. The sun had gone behind the mountains but the sky was brightly beautiful. The three paused to drink in the loveliness, then turned and went indoors. Koopah soon glanced anxiously at Alea. There she was, sitting silently as she watched her father busy about the house. Coming home without her mother must be even more bewildering to her than to him. He, too, was sad—but Alea was younger. What could he do to bring back her laughter?

Looking down at his blistered hands that were now smarting and itching, he gave a deep groan. "Poor Koopah," he moaned. "Poor, poor Koopah. He pulls a big boat home. His hands get so sore they are almost worn through and no one pays any attention to them. Ooh! Ooh!"

Alea ran across the room to look at his palms. Why, they were not nearly in such bad shape as they had sometimes been in the past. The old faker! Patting his hands lovingly and gently, she said softly, "Poor Koopah, his hands are almost worn right to the bones, with the worst blisters Alea ever saw. She must fix them."

Suddenly she squeezed his hand tightly, which made Koopah yell in pain that was no sham. Alea laughed merrily.

Ahpea glanced up with a warm, glad smile. Trust Koopah to find a way to cheer Alea! He himself had realized what those groans were for and by the tussle that was going on right now, he knew Alea would be all right. Koopah would not let her be lonely.

Time passed. Busy day followed busy day. Daylight became ever shorter and the long dark nights closed in early. Many hours were spent watching and waiting for seals that seldom were seen, or were too far away for the rifles.

Alea found little time to be idle. Her father tried to have her with him as much as possible, often hunting by boat instead of going inland, to save her from walking too far. Koopah roved the land in search of deer, but he saw none. Ahpea went on hunting trips, leaving the other two at home. All too frequently he came home with nothing more than a rabbit or an occasional hare or partridge.

"I'll be glad when the snows come and the foxes get prime. I hope we have a snowfall soon," he said, one evening.

His wish was fulfilled more quickly than he expected. The next morning when they looked out, the ground was covered with snow and the white flakes were still coming down heavily. Alea dressed warmly and went out to the water's edge. She could not see through the grayness that shut her in like a curtain, and she laughed to feel the snowflakes falling cold on her upturned face.

Alea stood quietly on the shore. It was late fall, always

heavy with fog. The quack of the eider ducks was near, yet the birds themselves were not visible in their shelter of thick weather. The cry of sea gulls echoed eerily as they dove for bits of fish or mussels spewed up by seals or whales. The smell of salty seaweed was everywhere. Alea heard the splash of a seal, safe now in its cover of fog and snow. How she loved it all!

When Alea went back to the house, she was covered with snow. A cold blast followed her as she opened the door.

"Hey! Don't bring all that snow in," cried Koopah. "I just swept the floor!"

He had indeed been busy. All three shared the work of keeping the house, even doing very well in taking care of their clothes.

Just before the bay froze over, Koopah had killed a seal with his new rifle. Now the skin was cleaned and spread out to dry. This would be first to go toward paying the big debt Ahpea owed at the trading post, and they hoped they would have many more to take to the trader next summer. They were very glad for this good start in their hunting.

As the days went by, there was joy in their hearts and laughter on their lips as they worked and talked. This, they knew, was as Soona would have it. Thought of her was close in all that they did—their beloved Soona, their dear, dear Soona.

6

WINTER ACTIVITIES

It was Alea who caught the first fox of the season. Her face was glowing with cold and excitement when she brought it in, a large red one. And there were exclamations of pride and admiration as Ahpea and Koopah examined it.

"It is a fine one, a very, very fine one, Alea. I am proud of you, my daughter," said Ahpea.

But Koopah never lost an opportunity to tease. He, too, was proud that Alea had caught this fine fox but he did not say so. Instead, he screwed up his eyes, pursed up his lips, rocked on his heels, and with his hands behind his back, said slowly, "It's too bad it is such a small fox. It must have been sleeping under a rock and forgot to grow up."

He was about to go on, but Alea's face showed such utter disappointment that he caught her in a hug and rocked her back and forth, saying, "It *is* a big fox! Koopah is just an old teaser. It is a bigger one than any I caught all last year."

Koopah and Alea chatted and laughed as they watched their father clean and spread the fox pelt on the board. When, two days later, it was taken off and turned right side out, they were ecstatically happy. The fox was well furred and its tail was full and soft.

Each evening brought its tasks. There were always their clothes, wet from the melting snow, to be put up to dry. Sealskin boots became hard when they dried and must be softened with the teeth before they could be turned right side out.

Koopah was never happy over this chewing of his boots. He would complain with utter disgust, "My teeth don't like these old boots. I'm tired of biting and chewing on this hard skin. I think I'll just wear them as they are, inside out."

This brought delighted laughter from Alea, who enjoyed putting Koopah through difficult tasks that she, herself, disliked as much as he did. In times past, this work had been done by Soona. Now they must all work to keep their clothes fit for everyday use.

Ahpea did not shirk his share of drying and chewing his boots. He worked quietly, contentedly listening to the teasing and banter of these two who brought joy and comfort to his home. But upon occasion, he joined in their discussions, was ever ready with advice, and was never too tired to instruct or encourage them. Sometimes he even joined in their games, with laughter that was sincere and infectious.

They saw no other people all that winter. Their hunting place was out of the way of other trappers and since they had no dogs or sled, they were unable to go very far. All their hunting was done on foot. Ahpea made up his mind that next year they must have a dog team.

Many times they walked far away from the shore, searching for caribou and staying overnight. They were often so weary they camped early, building an igloo by cutting snow blocks and warming it with heat from a stone lamp and moss wick and seal fat. They would rest through the night and then start out again early the next morning.

Often their search was in vain. Other times they would kill a deer and go home with plenty of good meat, sometimes so much that several trips were required in order to carry it all home. There were times, too, when the foxes and wolves beat them to the meat they had necessarily left behind and what they took home on the first trip was all they got.

Other days, they cut holes through the thick ice in the lakes and were quick to spear the fish that came swimming lazily along, deep down in the water. The trout were brought wriggling and twisting to the surface to be cast free on the ice, where they froze stiff, ready to be taken home by the hunters. This was sport they all loved.

There were stormy days when blizzards raged over the land and no one ventured outside. On such days Ahpea, assisted by gaily chatting Koopah and Alea, busied himself with mending and making hunting gear. After the wind had blown itself out, they would look at the scene before them and marvel at the change. There would be a snow bank where none had been before, or a bank which had towered high before the storm was completely gone and all was now level and flat.

One day they followed the stream that ran by their home. The snow covered most of the ice, but here and there were patches of clear blue ice. They hunted all day but saw nothing except a few rabbit tracks. They were about to turn homeward when Ahpea suddenly grabbed Koopah's arm and motioned him to get down and be quiet. Alea crouched down and followed her father's gaze. Yes —over there at the edge of the shore something was moving!

"Atata, what is it?" Alea whispered.

"Otters," her father told her softly. "We can get near enough to shoot them if they don't see us before they go beneath the ice. They have holes down there somewhere near the shore. Don't move until I give you the sign; then run when I do."

Ahpea kept his voice low, for he knew that the otters had sharp ears and might hear him.

Breathlessly the three watched the four otters playing and cavorting on the hillside. They looked like seals, slick and shiny, but, unlike the seal, they had long tails. The small animals slowly climbed uphill, then came down at great speed.

Alea covered her mouth to keep from laughing out loud. What fun they were having, climbing up, then sliding down again, getting completely buried in the deep snow at the bottom of the slide! The otters would poke their heads up, look at each other comically, then race off again in a great hurry. When they had apparently decided that they had had fun enough for one day, they went off down toward the shore to their feeding place. This brought them within rifle range of the watching hunters.

Bang! Bang! Two shots rang out and two otters floated on the water at the edge of the broken ice. Ahpea jumped to his feet and raced to secure his kill. Koopah and Alea ran too, while the other two otters escaped beneath the ice.

"We have two fine skins," Ahpea said happily. "No use hunting for the others now. They won't come out after hearing the shots. Otters are very wise. They will likely find a way to escape without being caught."

Alea was unusually quiet that evening as her father cleaned and spread the otters on the drying board. Ahpea was so engrossed in his work that he did not notice her silence.

Koopah, watching his father, said, "This is the first otter I ever killed."

"You made a good shot," Ahpea replied.

Koopah now realized that Alea, putting her wet mittens up to dry, was much too quiet. Was she ill? Then he saw that she was getting ready for bed earlier than usual.

"Want to go hunting for the otters with me tomorrow?" he asked her.

Alea shook her head without speaking.

"You tired or something?" he persisted, unhappy now, for he felt certain something was wrong.

Then to the surprise and distress of both her father and brother, Alea covered her face with her hands and burst into tears.

Ahpea went to a basin and washed his hands. After

drying them, he took Alea's arm and drew her to him. "What happened to our little woman? Did we work her too hard today?" he asked tenderly.

"No," she sobbed.

"What is it then?"

"They were so happy. They were sliding and looking at each other. Now they are dead," she wailed.

Ahpea was too surprised to speak. He certainly did not expect tears because he had gotten two fine otter skins. What could he say to Alea, who was crying because the otters were dead? He wished her mother were here to help him. Soona would have known how to explain to their daughter that even little otters must be used for food and skins in order that human beings might live. Yet here was Alea crying about them. He felt bewildered and glanced at Koopah, but there was no help there this time. Koopah was staring open-mouthed at his sister, who cried over a dead otter. If she cried about that, what would she do if they killed a bear?

Koopah could not think of a thing to say.

He heard his father telling Alea, "We hunt animals because they are our living. With the skins, we buy the supplies that we need. The meat is our food. We do not kill because we like hurting them. We must have many skins to take to the trader next summer."

"But they were playing," Alea sobbed.

"All animals play sometimes . . . bear, wolves, foxes . . . everything."

"Wolves and bears play?" she asked, looking up in surprise.

"Yes, Alea, even wolves and bears."

Feeling comforted, she dried her eyes. Ahpea went back to his work.

Alea looked at Koopah, who still appeared puzzled about the cause of the tears and sat saying nothing. "I'll go with you tomorrow to hunt the otters," she told him, thinking he might not want her now because of her crying.

Koopah blew out his breath in exaggerated relief. "We'll go after that ol' otter that made Alea cry. I'll blow him right out of the lake," he said with a grin.

Koopah did not shoot the otters the next day, for the wise animals had made good their escape during the night. There were only the wide tracks in the soft snow to show that by now the little animals were safely far out of reach, too far for the eager hunters to pursue them without a dog team.

Ahpea declared, "Yes, next year we must have a dog team. When we go to Aiviktok I will try to get a sled and dogs. Many trappers have more dogs than they need."

The days of this first winter without Soona went quickly for the busy family. Then it was nearing spring. The snow melted from the warmth of the sun by day and froze solid at night.

One night Ahpea was repairing a broken spear. Koopah was turning his wet boots inside out to dry for the next day, when he saw that the old patch was coming loose and certainly would not keep out moisture.

Muttering in disgust, he said, "This ol' patch is loose. It's not going to keep the water out and some day I'm going to get my feet even more wet than today and freeze all my toes off and then I'll hop along like a fox on three legs."

He heard a gasp and looked up to see Alea with her hands pressed against her mouth, her eyes fixed on the offending boot. "I'll fix it, Koopah. You must not get your feet frozen. I'll fix it now."

He tried to tell her he was only joking and his feet had not really been wet. But she was satisfied only when she took the old patch off and sewed on a new one. Long into the night she worked. This was for Koopah. Her own Koopah. The boots were well mended when Koopah wore them the next day.

Boots were hard to make. The thick, hard skin was difficult to sew. Soona had been a good bootmaker and had given Alea a number of lessons in the work. It was a big task for the girl, and she spent many hours at it.

Alea grew greatly that year and was happy only when she was helping the others with the hunting and the household tasks. Her laughter was gay and she tried in all ways to take the place of her mother for these two she loved so much.

7

AIVIKTOK

SPRING CAME with its bright sunshine. The ice was bared of its winter snow covering. Lying on the ice in quiet bays, seals basked in the sun. Tirelessly, Ahpea and Koopah and Alea hunted them, but the seals were wily. They were keen of ear and eye. The least sound of cracking ice, a cough, or a sneeze was enough to send them down where no one could get near them. The little family were often weary and empty-handed as they trudged homeward. Only occasionally were patience and perseverance rewarded by success.

Then the ice broke up and the water was open once more. Ahpea examined his boat for leaks. He melted tar over fire and put it into the cracks in the boat that had been made by the frost. Koopah then ran a heated iron over other damaged places.

Alea quietly watched all this. She liked the smell of the hot tar. She also liked the freshness of approaching summer, the scent of the spruce and pine trees that filled the air, the unfolding of tiny green leaves on the willows.

Soon there would be the sound of the larks and sparrows nesting on the cliffs or on some sheltered willow bough.

"We go to Aiviktok as soon as our boat is ready," Koopah told her.

"Yes, Atata said so," she answered.

Four days later the boat was launched and, to their satisfaction, it did not leak. They were ready for the trip to the trading post. They put the precious bundle of skins in the boat—not so many as Ahpea had had last year, but he hoped there were enough to pay off the debt he owed the trader. That would make him happy. It did not matter that his hands were calloused and hard from working. He was glad for this day when he was on his way to turn his furs over to the kind trader.

The rowing was hard, with a headwind all the way so that, as had so often happened before, they could not use the sail. They camped at night in some sheltered cove. Ahpea set a net and caught three large salmon, which made Alea exclaim with delight. The fish were cleaned, cut up and cooked for their supper. Then Koopah amazed his father by making an excellent batch of flapjacks, browned to perfection on a flat rock over a low fire. His eyes sparkled with happiness at Ahpea's enjoyment and praise. He stole a glance at Alea and saw there was no doubt of her satisfaction, for on the rock which was her plate she had a huge piece of salmon and her mouth was full of flapjack. She was enjoying her meal to the fullest.

They were not the first to arrive at the trading post. As they approached, they could see many boats and kayaks lining the landing beach in front of the trader's house.

People came flocking down to meet Ahpea's boat. The wives and daughters of the trappers always had something new to wear and be admired when the boats came in. It was truly a gala time of dressing up for their annual get-together and visiting and exchanging of news and yarns.

Alea jumped ashore as soon as the boat grounded. She smiled happily at the many familiar faces of those she knew and loved. She looked like a boy. She had long outgrown her own clothes and was now dressed in Koopah's last year's trousers and coat. She did not mind having no new clothes for this dress-up occasion and was conscious only that she was happy to see all her friends.

She heard the greetings, "Glad to see you! Where were you in that big storm last winter? Wasn't that one bad wind?"

Another was saying, "I lost my traps—buried under snow. Didn't find them 'til the snow melted."

And how delighted Alea and her brother and father were to see Mrs. Jamieson in the welcoming crowd.

Mrs. Jamieson drew Alea close. "You have grown much, my wee one," she said in Alea's Eskimo language. "I can see that your two men have cared for you well."

Alea nodded. "But it is good to be here with you now," she replied. "Where is your man?"

"In the post," Mrs. Jamieson told her, "looking over supplies to buy."

While Ahpea took his furs to the trader's store, Alea and Koopah visited in the tents of friends.

During their four days' stay, Ahpea was able to buy four young dogs and a sled. He was well pleased with this, for now he would soon have a trained team. He was also happy because his skins had been sufficient to settle his debt to the trader, and even to pay for some new supplies. He still owed for the boat, but his friend, Jamieson, assured him there was no hurry, and Ahpea knew he would be able to complete the payment next summer.

Then came the last night at the trading post for most of the trappers. Next morning, they would start back to their hunting places for another year. On this last night the postmaster always gave a dance for everyone to enjoy. The large boathouse was cleaned out and made ready. Everyone gathered there that night to take part or simply to watch. Bill Anderson, a young trapper and also an interpreter between Eskimos and white trappers who could not understand each other's language, brought out his accordion and played for the dancers. The women wore their gayest dresses and tied bright ribbons in their braided hair.

Reels, quadrilles and schottisches were in order. Boys and girls changed partners; old and young danced together far into the night. No one danced more than Koopah. He stepped out in expert time and never lacked for partners. He danced with all the girls and women. His buoyant spirit and flashing black eyes drew smiles as he swung in and out.

Ahpea and Alea sat on empty barrels in a corner and silently laughed at Koopah's enjoyment. Alea's face glowed with love and admiration as she leaned against the wall by her father. Quiet and reserved, preferring to watch, she took no active part in the fun.

Toward the end of the evening, when the floor was

cleared for a change of partners, and couples were taking their places for a new dance, the caller signaled that two more were needed. A young man moved out to the vacant place as his eyes went quickly over the room in search of a partner. He was named Yorgke and had come with his father from up the coast.

A good-looking half-breed girl, Tamanna, stepped up to him. "Come on, Yorgke, we dance this one," she said.

But Yorgke still looked the room over. "Wait, I'm looking for someone," he told her.

When he saw Alea over by the wall, he went quickly over to her side. "Will you dance this with me?" he asked.

Alea shook her head. "No, no. I don't know how to dance."

"Come on," urged Yorgke. "Let me see you try. Then if you can't dance, I'll believe you." He tried to take her arm.

"I can't! I can't! I'm not dressed up," insisted Alea.

Yorgke looked down at her boy's clothes. Why had she not dressed up like the other people? Yes, she was right that she could not step out looking like a boy, but what was the idea?

He called to the dancers, "Go ahead. Fill up the floor. I'm sitting this one out."

Tamanna had followed Yorgke to see for whom he was looking. She herself was the most sought-after girl at the post. The best-dressed, too. And she was provoked by his offhand slight. Her lip turned up disdainfully when she saw Yorgke asking this girl in boy's clothes to be his partner in the dance.

"Was she the one you were looking for?" she asked, with scorn in her voice. "She'd look funny dancing in those clothes. My mother says she is growing up wild like the foxes up the bay with just men around. Better watch out, Yorgke, she might bite you." And she walked off with a swagger and a toss of her head.

Alea, much distressed, exclaimed, "Oh, now you missed the dance!"

Yorgke looked at her searchingly and said, "I don't mind that. I'd rather talk to you. Why didn't you dress up for the dance? I saw you just watching and thought you would dance with me."

"I'd rather hunt than dance," Alea told him. "I was too busy to think of dressing up last winter."

"Are you happy?" he asked, looking at her curiously. There seemed something pathetic about this girl. She was very young, yet oddly reserved and shy. She radiated health and animation, but there was that sober look in her dark eyes that might belong to a much older person.

"Yes, my Atata, Koopah and I had a good winter up the bay. We did well with skins."

"Where was your mother? Is she here?"

"No, she was lost last summer."

The answer was so low he had to bend his head to hear it.

He was silent for some time, then asked, "Was Soona your mother?"

She nodded her head.

Now he knew who this girl was. Everyone had heard of Ahpea's loss. Yorgke's family lived some distance away from them but even there they had heard about the tragedy.

Ahpea had moved away from his place on the barrel as Yorgke came up. But he had been close enough to hear Tamanna snub Alea. And he was strangely disturbed by the conversation between Alea and Yorgke. It was true that, living alone with Koopah and him, Alea was not like other young girls. Tonight she was not joining in the fun because she felt strange and did not want to. But she should want to. True, she was happy as she was, but this was not as it should be. How could she know how to take a woman's place later if she did not learn to do so as she grew up? With genuine alarm, Ahpea realized that his daughter would be, as Tamanna's mother had said, wild like the foxes. Alea needed a woman's care.

Deep in thought, he left the building and went in search of his friends, the Jamiesons. He wanted some advice and knew he would get it from them.

Jamieson was reading and looked up as Ahpea entered his tent. "Ahpea, why is it you are not dancing with the bonnie lassies down at the boat shed?" the Scotchman asked.

Ahpea smiled as he answered, "I did not see you down there."

Jamieson stole a sly glance to make sure his wife could hear him and, putting his hand to his mouth, said in a loud whisper, "Lad, I went to a dance once and got hooked."

Mrs. Jamieson stood up, her hands on her wide hips. "You lie, mon," she retorted. "I did not get you at any dance. You looked so lonely staring down into a barrel of herring I was scared you'd drown yourself and married you to save your life."

They all laughed over this good-natured banter. Then the conversation became more serious and Ahpea laid his problem before them.

"I don't know what to do about Alea," he said.

Mrs. Jamieson, immediately concerned, asked, "What's wrong with the lass?"

"There is nothing wrong with her. She is well and happy."

Then Ahpea told them what he had heard and seen to-night, about Tamanna and what her mother had said. "Alea did not join in the fun," he concluded. "She did not want to. She is satisfied as she is, to be just like a boy. I want her to be like other girls."

Mrs. Jamieson was thoughtful for a while; then she suggested that Ahpea take a married couple up the bay with them. "If Alea associates with only men, as she is now doing with you and Koopah, she will know only men's ways. She needs a woman to teach her how to be a woman. You will be able to find a couple, I am sure. There are some people who prefer to hire out their services rather than have a place of their own. There's that man Palliseer, for instance. He's no good as a hunter but he has a fine wife. She's a fine woman, a smart sewer, too, and tidy. She would be just the one for you if he is not already hired out to some trapper."

Jamieson scratched his rugged chin whimsically as he said, "Aye, the wife seems good enough but I don't care for the mon. He is a slippery cuss and not worth his salt.

But it's the woman you need and she'll be good for the lass. I'd say take them if you can get them."

Feeling relieved, Ahpea left the tent and went in search of the Palliseers. He knew the man by sight but had never had any dealings with him. He understood Palliseer was half Indian and half French, never getting many furs but helping out wherever he got a place to stay for the winter. A drifter. Well, it did not matter so much about the man, as Mrs. Jamieson said. It was the woman Ahpea needed for Alea.

He found the Palliseers in the boathouse watching the dancers. Yes, the wife was a small, neatly dressed Eskimo woman of nice appearance.

Ahpea approached them with a cordial smile, at once asking the man, "How would you like to go up the bay and live with me this winter?"

"Don' keer if I do," the man answered without taking his eyes off the dancers. "When you go?" he asked. "And what you pay?"

"In the morning, early," Ahpea answered shortly, going on to outline the terms he had in mind. Palliseer quickly agreed to them.

The wife heard but she made no comment. There was nothing to say. It was always this way. She was used to obeying quietly. She would pack and be ready in the morning.

When Ahpea informed Koopah and Alea that he had asked Palliseer and his wife to come and live with them, they objected strongly. Ahpea tried patiently to explain that this was for Alea, but Alea declared rebelliously, "I like me as I am. I don't need to be shown how to be a woman!"

Ahpea held steadfastly to his decision. But as he went to bed that night, he wondered what would happen between the Palliseers and Koopah and Alea when they met in the morning.

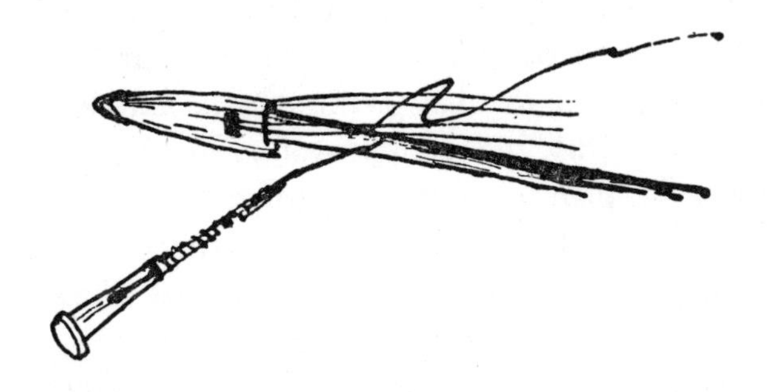

8

PALLISEER

WHEN Koopah and Alea arrived at the boat the next morning they looked at the Palliseers with resentful eyes. There the couple stood on the shore with all their belongings, waiting to go up the bay with Ahpea and his family. Ahpea felt keenly the disapproval of his young people and hoped his plan was not going to be a failure.

However, Alea was delighted with the young dogs as they were put into the boat. They wagged their tails in happy response as she petted each one.

"Oh, look at this one, Koopah!" she exclaimed. "It is all black but its feet are white, just like boots. And this one is red, even its nose. I think its eyes must be red, too, but he's too sleepy to open them." She laughed in her joy over them.

"They are all fine pups and will soon grow up into a fine team," Ahpea said, glad that the sight of the pups had made her happy and that the tenseness of the moment seemed forgotten.

With the two extra people, the new sled and supplies for the winter, the boat was heavily loaded. Once more there was little wind and the rowing was long and difficult. Palliseer took his turn at the oars and seemed willing to help in any way needed.

Ahpea found himself wondering about this man who seemed to have no desire to be an independent trapper but was content to hire out his services. So far as Ahpea knew, Palliseer always found a place with some industrious trapper and hunted in a leisurely fashion. Ahpea observed the strong hands showing white knuckles as the man pulled on the oars. He noted the dark, swarthy features, the thin lips and high cheekbones that were his inheritance from his Indian mother, his straight black hair and the small black eyes that even now shifted as they caught Ahpea's direct gaze fixed speculatively on him.

Ahpea felt his face redden as he realized he had been staring at the man and had made him feel uncomfortable. Quickly he said, "It is getting late. Let us go ashore in that sheltered cove and put up for the night. We have pulled enough for today."

Koopah jumped out and pulled the boat in. The tents were pitched and the boat's contents taken inside. The Palliseers' tent was small, but it was shelter against the wind and rain that came up during the night. Alea heard her father go outside to fasten down the boat, but she was lulled back to sleep by the noise of the pattering rain.

It was two days before the storm eased and they were able to continue their journey. On the last day of the trip, Alea was very tired from rowing. She found comfort in watching the wake of the boat as it moved through the water, for if the boat were still, there would be no wake.

It was because they were moving ahead that it was there, so another pull and another p—

A hand covered hers. Startled, she glanced up quickly to see the wife of Palliseer smiling down at her.

"It is Selalu's turn. You have been at the oars a long time. Let me pull now."

Alea let the woman take her place and moved back by her father. This was the first time the woman had spoken to her. Alea was shy and had left her alone. She had been watching the woman but had not yet made up her mind about her. Selalu was good to look at. Her face was round and full and she had soft, kind dark eyes. Her hair was always neatly braided. She seemed very quiet and spoke only when addressed directly. Yes, Alea now decided, she liked Selalu.

After they arrived home, trees were cut down and an addition put onto their house to make a bedroom for the Palliseers. A doorway was cut through to the large outer room, which was living quarters for them all. Over in the corner was Alea's bed, sheltered by a curtain. She had always felt this to be her private room, respected by her father and Koopah as her own. No one went behind that curtain but herself. It did not matter that Koopah, too, shared the same room. His bed also had a curtain. The only wooden door in the house was the outside one, and anyone who lifted the latch of Ahpea's unlocked outside door was welcome in his home.

So the Palliseers began their life with the family up the bay, hunting, trapping, fishing, and helping out in any way needed. Bad weather sometimes kept Alea indoors. On such days Selalu assisted her with the care of their clothes. Under the woman's expert guidance, Alea learned to pattern and make clothes for the men and herself. She enjoyed Selalu's companionship, and a warm affection grew between them. Selalu found Alea's escapades amusing and liked her shy modesty. Alea was more venturesome than Selalu, who spent many anxious hours waiting for Alea to come home when sudden storms came up and the girl was still away. Whenever Alea returned, Selalu would beat the snow from the girl's clothes, warm her cold hands and fuss over her like a happy mother. Alea responded with a joyous heart as she told of the day's happenings, and together they would romp with the dogs.

Seeing Alea's happiness with Selalu, Aphea was well pleased that he had decided to bring the Palliseers into their home—though, to be sure, the man was a poor trapper and often neglected his traps, which would get iced in and would not spring while the foxes stole the bait. Then, much to Koopah's amusement, Palliseer complained loudly about the "bad year for the fox."

Once Koopah teased him about it. "I saw one of your traps today," said the boy, "so iced in that even a bear couldn't strike it up. When did you set it last?"

Palliseer did not like the joke and retorted, "I fix my traps plenty good. No need for you to tell me how to fix them."

Seeing his angry scowl, Koopah shrugged his shoulders and walked away. He did not like Palliseer very well.

That winter and the next and the next passed in the usual manner. The seasons came and went. There were the yearly short trips to the post for supplies. Alea grew up. She never wore a dress and had the appearance of a well-built young man. A good shot with the rifle, she trapped and hunted ceaselessly. She was unafraid and full of the love of adventure. Yet, on the short trips to the trading post, she was shy and reserved.

Then somehow Alea began to feel worried and anxious. She did not tell the others about it, but she was getting an intense dislike of Palliseer. Outwardly nothing was changed, yet she was more and more certain he was dishonest. She could not forget something that had happened last winter . . . a thing she had seen yet could not prove, so she kept it to herself and said nothing.

It happened one stormy day when, with her spyglass in hand, she had climbed high up the mountain side to look for deer tracks. Far across the valley she had sighted a man taking a fox from a trap. At first she could not see him distinctly through the storm. When the wind eased, she saw him again. It was Palliseer. She watched him walk hurriedly away with the dead fox in his hand.

She knew that was Koopah's trap and felt glad that Palliseer was taking the fox home. It might have cut its leg off and got away before Koopah revisited his trap.

When she arrived home a little later she found her father and Selalu admiring the fine red fox Palliseer said he had caught in his own trap. He did not tell them it was Koopah's fox.

Impulsively Alea said, "I saw you take the fox out of the trap. It was on Big Lookout Mountain with my spyglass."

She was surprised at the anger in his face as he cut her short. "You did not see Palliseer from Big Lookout Mountain! My traps are up the other way!"

"But I did see you."

When he glared at her so fiercely and looked so black in his anger, she fell silent.

Her father, glancing up from his work, smiled at her as he said, "My daughter must have been blinded with snow drift to see a man where he was not."

Alea said no more, but her suspicion that Palliseer had stolen Koopah's fox was confirmed when she heard Koopah that evening telling Ahpea, "Amagok, wolf, must have gotten to my trap today before I did. It was struck up and there was blood on the snow, but it had drifted and there were no tracks or fur so it must have been dragged away."

She lay in her bed that night trying to understand what had happened. Her father would be much disturbed if she accused Palliseer of stealing that fox. It was just her word against Palliseer's, and he had already denied that he had been at Koopah's trap that day.

It was a dreadful thing to accuse a person of stealing or cheating. She had never known a bad person in her life, and now she was sure Palliseer was a bad man, a thief. He had taken Koopah's fox. She couldn't tell Koopah about it because he would be angry and face Palliseer with it, and then there would be trouble. She was afraid this bad man might hurt Koopah in his anger. This must be her secret, the first she had ever had from her family, but it was for them she must keep to herself what she knew.

She would avoid Palliseer as much as possible, and not even tell Selalu. Alea loved her and it would make Selalu very unhappy to know her husband was a thief.

So it was that Alea went about her hunting and work in her usual way. But she held no conversation with Palliseer and avoided any contact with him. If it had not been that sometimes, on looking up suddenly, she caught him watching her slyly, she might have forgotten the episode; but those furtive glances always renewed her dislike of him.

Time passed and spring came again. Robins and larks were nesting in the trees or high up in the cliffs. Koopah, now grown into a tall young man, yet still with the buoyant spirit of the boy, had gone inland to the lake to look for geese that might be migrating north. Alea had at first thought she would go with him, but later changed her mind and decided to hunt birds' nests instead.

It was late in the evening that she was going along the hillside. She had spent the day climbing the cliffs and finding nests. Although the tiny eggs looked tempting and she would have liked to hold them in her hand, she was satisfied to know the nests were there and to go on looking for still more.

Hearing the sound of breaking twigs, she glanced down and saw the grinning face of Palliseer looking up at her.

"Come down. You won't find any nests up there. Soon be dark," he called.

She made no answer. What was he doing here? Her heart was pounding and again she felt fear of him and distrust. Slowly, quietly she began to move away from where he stood. She tried to control her desire to run. He was watching her work her way downhill. He knew she did not like him and this made him all the more determined to demonstrate who was master of this situation. He was not going to be ignored by this girl. She should not escape that easily. She was alone now and he'd show her.

Palliseer came running and stood squarely in Alea's path. She could not get around him. He gloated that she would have to notice him now. He was perfectly aware she had despised him since that time when he had stolen Koopah's fox. He had never understood why she had not told her father or Koopah about it.

She started to run back, but he overtook her, catching her roughly by the arm and saying mockingly, "Wait, don't hurry so much. We'll talk, yes?"

"No! Go away! Let me go!" she stormed, her eyes blazing with fear and anger.

"What's the matter? You shy maybe?" He laughed at her efforts to free herself from his grasp. "You think Eskimo girl better than Indian man, maybe?"

As she fought desperately to free her arm, he laughed. "Ho, ho, ho. She fights like a fox in trap."

At the mention of a fox in a trap, Alea stopped struggling and looked straight into his face. He knew she was remembering the fox he had stolen from Koopah.

Suddenly his face turned ugly and black with anger and he snarled at her, "If you ever tell Koopah or your father about the fox, I'll kill them, see? You tell them I talk to you now, I'll kill you too!"

He suddenly flung her to the ground and she screamed

in her terror. "Koopah! Koopah!" It was not that Koopah could hear her, but because she had never needed him as she needed him now.

Palliseer's face was evil. He grabbed her again to pull her to her feet, but she bit his hand and he dropped her. She lay on the ground crying.

Then from some distance came Koopah's shout. "Alea! Alea! Whoo-ee. Where are you?"

"Koopah! Koopah!" she screamed.

Looking around quickly to see if he were observed, Palliseer muttered a last threat, "I kill him if you tell," and crept off into the darkness.

"Alea! Whoo-ee!" called Koopah, sounding much nearer now. He could not see her for the brushwood and the rocks.

Alea picked herself up. She was still crying, but one thought was uppermost. She must not let Koopah know about her struggle with Palliseer. The man had said he would kill if she told, and she believed he really would. She was filled with a great fear of this bad man.

Koopah came running up as she stood trembling with her hands pressed against her face.

"Alea, are you hurt? What made you scream? I heard you way up there."

Alea could not stop shaking. She tried to smile but the tears still spilled over. Koopah held her in his arms and felt great concern as he looked at her.

"Did you fall down the cliff? Did a wolf chase you or something?"

"No, I got frightened . . . too far from home or something," she sobbed.

"You too far from home? That's not why you screamed. You would never have screamed for such a reason. Tell me what happened."

She took his hand and put it against her face. "Oh, Koopah, it is good you got back from the lake. Hold me hard. Don't leave me."

Holding his sister in his arms, he looked deep into her eyes. He was not satisfied, but he knew she had told him all she would now. He must be content to know she was safe. Something had happened to frighten her. If she did not want to tell him, he would not add to her trouble by forcing her to talk about it. He held her hand as they walked home.

Ahpea looked up as they entered and asked Koopah, "Where is that goose you went after?"

Koopah laughed and told him, "It is still flying away from Koopah." He said nothing about Alea.

Selalu was there with her happy smile, busily sewing, as was her custom. There was no sign of Palliseer.

Alea was unhappy. For the first time in her life she was living in fear of a man her father thought was their friend. And, too, he was Selalu's man. No one but herself knew he was bad, and she could not tell her family what she knew. She must protect them from Palliseer, who had threatened her and who was a thief, yet shared their home and made Ahpea believe he was a good man. She could not confide in her father and her brother because she loved them so much. Silence was the only way to keep them safe.

9

A THIEF STEALS AGAIN

WHEN Ahpea's boat next reached Aiviktok, they found the traders' supply ship had already been there and was gone again. They were sorry to miss it, for the annual arrival of the vessel from London was a big event. They did their trading and then prepared for the trip home.

It was the evening before they were to leave, and Ahpea pondered a problem that was bothering him considerably. It was the persistent thought that Alea should go away to school. Some of the trappers sent their sons and daughters to London to learn to read and write, for there were no schools near enough on the Labrador for them to attend. These young people who went away were much respected and admired, when they came back and told of wonderful things they had seen in the land of the ship's people—the English sailors on the trading ship. Ahpea had just heard that Yorgke, the young man of the dance episode, had gone to get some learning in London.

Ahpea had never forgotten the time Tamanna had snubbed Alea at the dance and had repeated her mother's words that Alea would be "wild like the foxes" living up the bay with just Koopah and himself. He did not want his Alea ever to be snubbed again.

Ahpea's eyes were loving as they rested on Alea, who at this moment was nearby, playing with a fat baby. She was laughing merrily as she helped the toddling child walk to its adoring mother. Yes, Alea was getting to be a young woman. Whatever he was going to do about sending her to school should be done soon. She still ran races with Koopah, set traps, chopped wood, was an experienced hunter, wore men's clothing, and made all her own clothes and his and Koopah's, too. He knew that Alea asked for nothing more than to go on living as she had up to now. She was keen and intelligent, but she could not read or write or say more than a few words of the language of the ship's people. He did not want her to know less than other trappers' daughters.

He had done well with skins since the time he lost his boat and Soona. He even had furs he had not yet sold and money saved up. There would not be any charge for passage on the boat, Mr. Jamieson had assured him, since it was just a supply ship from England, and that is where Alea would have to go, for the ship made no stops after it left Aiviktok on its return to its home port of London.

Ahpea knew Alea would not want to go away alone. Well, he might even take her himself. He would see next year.

The Palliseers still shared their home up the bay. Yesterday Alea had surprised Ahpea by saying, "This time, when we return, let us leave the Palliseers behind. We don't need them now."

When he had looked at her questioningly and said, "You like Selalu. Is it Palliseer you don't like?" she had seemed embarrassed.

Turning away, she had replied, "I liked the time best when we were alone—just you, Koopah and me."

Ahpea put all his perplexing thoughts away, doing nothing about breaking connection with the Palliseers. Back again, they went into a busy summer, glad the trip to the trading post was over and they were home for another season.

Fall weather came again. At night the ice formed in a thin shell around the rocks, and it melted in the heat of the sun by day. Alea loved the boating and fishing and was out on the bay every day when there was no storm. She thrilled to think that soon winter would come again and they could hunt and travel once more with the sled and dog team.

One day she rowed far down the bay to find a good place to fish. She caught a fine lot of cod and was very happy. Selalu would help clean and hang them to dry in the sun.

A long, low whistle made her look ashore. There was Palliseer, sitting on a rock, watching her. He motioned for her to come in. Why was he there? She knew he could not reach her, for he had no boat; but Alea felt the old fear of him rise swiftly. All the brightness of the day seemed to fade. Pulling in her line, she started quickly homeward. The man laughed and called out after her, "Hey, don't go away." But she went on.

That evening she heard her father and Palliseer discussing the day. Palliseer said, "I went to see if I could find the fox trap I lost last year, but it was nowhere about."

She knew he was not telling her father the truth because he had been far down the bay, where she had seen him, and not inland, where his traps were. Palliseer saw Alea's eyes fixed on him and sent a leering smile in her direction.

Often while lying in her bed, Alea would hear him moving about in the big room and be filled with renewed fear of him. She would cover her head with the blankets and hold her breath until he had passed on.

She decided to get farther away from the sound of Palliseer, and so it was that her father came home one evening to find her moving her bed, with Selalu's help, into a corner of his room.

"Alea is lonely. I want to be with you," she replied when he sought an explanation.

"If you want to sleep in my room, my daughter, I will help you move your bed, but your bed has always been where it is now—even when you were very young."

Ahpea did not understand this sudden whim to move the bed, but there was no reason why Alea should not do it. She had puzzled him once by crying because he killed the two otters and she puzzled him now. But he helped move the bed and curtain while Alea and Selalu joked and laughed as they carried in the blankets.

Koopah was the loudest in his surprise when he saw the empty corner where Alea's bed had been. "Hey, where's your bed?" he demanded.

Alea enjoyed his amazement and teased him. "Koopah snored so loud I could not sleep. I moved in with Atata."

Koopah stamped over to look in his father's room. Alea's bed had been in its corner ever since he could remember and he did not like the empty space it left.

"But why?" he asked.

When Alea saw the anxiety and concern in Koopah's face, she said softly, "Sometimes you are gone and the wind blows. Alea gets lonely, so I moved to be near Atata when you are away."

He knew that this was all the explanation he would get. But he was not satisfied. He wished to understand all that went on behind those dark eyes of his sister. He had seen terror in them a number of times after the two of them had been romping and laughing and could not understand it. There had been nothing to put the look there—no one had been in the room with them but Selalu and Palliseer. He was sure it could not be because of them. He knew how much Alea loved Selalu.

When winter came, Alea was seldom home before dark. Every day she tramped many miles on snowshoes to her traps. Occasionally she brought back a fox, some partridges or an Arctic hare. There were days, too, when she returned cold and empty-handed, her clothes damp from melting snow.

Then a great blizzard swept the land with its fury. No hunting was possible, and the family stayed in their shelter and waited for the storm to cease. One night Selalu, Alea, and Koopah got at the mending of the dog harnesses. They laughed and talked as they hurried to complete this difficult task. Koopah was the last to retire. As Alea lay in her bed she heard him moving about in the outer room. She was dozing off to sleep when she heard his boots drop to the floor with a thud as he prepared for bed. She shifted her position and soon was lulled to sleep by the sound of the snow beating against the house.

It was later in the night when she awoke with a start. Being a light sleeper, she was disturbed by some movement in the room. She raised her head and listened, but the only sound was of her father's regular breathing as he slept. She had cuddled down to sleep again when the sound of a furtive movement made her sit bolt upright. Quietly pushing her bed curtains aside, she peered out into the room.

At first, she saw nothing. Then, as her eyes became accustomed to the darkness, she made out the shadowy form of someone moving stealthily toward the doorway. Alea covered her mouth with her hand to stifle the scream that rose in her throat.

Palliseer was there in the room she shared with her father. She knew it was he. What was he doing? He had taken advantage of the noise of the storm to sneak in, for some reason. Now, believing himself unseen, he was leaving as silently as he had entered. She saw him go through the doorway without a sound. What had he come for?

Alea was unable to sleep any more that night. She shook with panic and could not control her fear of this man who prowled at night. She wanted to tell her father and Koopah what she knew, but always she came back to the memory of Palliseer's threatening harm to them if she revealed the secret. No, she could not tell them. She must keep this, too, to herself.

Koopah was disturbed at Alea's tired appearance the next morning and wanted to know if she was sick. When she said she had not slept well, he asked, "What did you do? Stay up all night?"

"No, the wind made too much noise. I couldn't sleep."

As she spoke a chill swept through her, for Palliseer was listening to what they were saying, his eyes fixed suspiciously on her face. He was probably wondering if she had seen him last night.

Koopah went on teasingly. "Oh, huh, I know what it was. You had growing pains. Even dogs get them. Our old leader had them last winter and used to howl terribly. Even kept the rest of the team awake with his old growing pains."

Koopah laughed aloud at his own joke, which made Alea laugh, too. Then, more seriously, he continued, "I think you are only hungry for a deer hunt with Koopah."

Alea said eagerly, "Oh, yes! Let us go now."

Koopah smiled and told her to look out at the storm, adding, "It will be fine tomorrow. The storm is nearly over. The deer will be hungry after the great blizzard. Yes, the toktu will be looking for moss on the flatlands."

Alea was delighted at the prospect of a deer hunt with Koopah. Selalu was her own helpful self and assisted in repairing the torn sleeping bag and in finishing the last harness so Alea could go to bed early and be rested for the next day.

They were still up that evening when Ahpea came out of his room and asked Alea if she had seen the box of cartridges which he kept on the shelf by his bed. She replied that she had not touched it.

"It was there, but I've looked everywhere and can't find it," Ahpea said anxiously.

Alea ran into the room, but came out saying, "It is not there, Atata."

Ahpea's face wore a perplexed frown as he said, "No, it is not there. I was sure I saw it last night, but it is gone now. I won't be able to go after deer or bears without cartridges for my rifle."

Koopah and Alea searched the other room. Selalu shook out Ahpea's bedding and looked in every corner for the missing box, but the cartridges could not be found. There was genuine consternation at the loss. Koopah's and Alea's rifles were different from Ahpea's. Now all Ahpea had with which to hunt was his shotgun and that would not do for big game.

Palliseer was loud in his surprise at Ahpea's loss. Shaking his head, he said, "Too bad. Too bad. Ahpea must have lost the cartridges in his sleep, yes?"

His regret was real to all but Alea. With narrowed eyes, she looked at Palliseer. He had a rifle like her father's and used the same kind of cartridges. He knew the box was there by her father's bed. It had been there all winter. They were low on ammunition and could not get more until next spring, when they would go to the trading post.

Alea was now sure that last night, under cover of darkness and the storm, Palliseer had sneaked into the room and stolen Ahpea's precious cartridges. She wished she could tell her father. Ahpea would never suspect the box was stolen. He would think that he had misplaced it somehow and was wrong in thinking it had been there last night. Only she knew that a thief had stolen again!

10

THE DEER HUNT

NEXT MORNING dawned clear and cold. The storm was over and it was with eager anticipation that Koopah and Alea arose early to get ready for the deer hunt. They loaded their sleeping bags and spare clothes on the sled and lashed them on securely.

The dogs, happy that they were going for a run, came trotting up to be harnessed. Until now, they had lain in the snow with the great storm raging about them. Shaking the ice from their fur, they gave short yelps of impatience to be off.

Alea was fastening the dogs' lines to the sled when she heard Palliseer say to her father, "I think I'll go along. Maybe I'll kill a deer."

Alea was gripped with a terror so great she could hardly breathe. Her father had his back to her and did not see her standing there, tense and still.

He answered, "Koopah and Alea don't want us along when they go to hunt the deer. They go alone. We must try for the fox while the weather stays cold. The fur will be turning and the skin no good when it gets mild."

Palliseer gave a short laugh. His sharp eyes had not missed Alea's fear.

"Don't stay away too long. Be careful of snowslides," Ahpea cautioned, when Alea and Koopah climbed onto the sled.

With an "Ooist-Ooist" they went off in a rush with the frisky dogs pulling the sled. Ahpea watched them go and threw up his hand in answer to Alea's waving hand.

They were able to ride most of the day until they reached the rough mountain country; then they had to go along the side of the hills to get to the inland where Koopah thought the deer might be found.

"We will go to the big plains. This is where the toktu feeds, beyond that mountain," he said.

Alea saw the mountain in the far distance and knew they must travel many miles to get to the deer. At last Koopah said they had come far enough for one day and they should make camp. Cutting out snow blocks and putting them together, he built an igloo. He had made many such snow houses, so it was not long until his dome-shaped hut was done. He came out the door so covered with snow that Alea laughed to see him.

"Our house is ready," he said, grinning at her and shaking himself. "Now you can fix the lamp while I feed the dogs."

Alea brought in the sleeping bags and spread them on the snow bed to sit on. Then she set up the stone lamp, put in the seal oil and arranged a strip of dried moss along the edge of the lamp for a wick. When she lit it she had trouble getting it to burn, but when Koopah came inside he found the house warm and comfortable and the lamp working fine.

"We have pepsi and nepko. Which do you want?" Koopah asked, as he unpacked the dried fish and dried meat Selalu had prepared for them to take on the trip.

"I want pepsi," Alea said. "A whole one. I'm so hungry I can eat bones and all." The pepsi, the dried trout, was a special treat.

Koopah smiled. This was food they liked and soon they were munching contentedly. On the morrow they hoped they might also have fresh deer meat.

They went to bed early and soon all was still and quiet. Once Koopah got up to see what was disturbing the dogs. He heard them growling and sniffing deep down in their throats. A long, drawn-out howl far away soon told Koopah there was a wolf on the prowl. Small wonder the dogs were restless. Going outside, he quieted them. By the light of the lamp, when he came back into the igloo, he saw Alea had not heard him go out. She was peacefully sleeping, cuddled up in her sleeping bag.

Next morning Alea stretched her arms drowsily and yawned as she awakened. Swoosh—a fur mitten hit her squarely on the jaw.

"What's that?" she screamed, diving down into the depths of her sleeping bag.

Hearing no sound, she slowly peered out to see Koopah, standing fully dressed, with laughter in his sparkling, mischievous eyes, ready to throw his other mitten at her surprised face. She ducked quickly and the shot went over her head.

"Oh, was that you?" he asked in mock amazement as she came up for air. "Koopah did not think it was alive. He did not know what that funny face was."

Then more seriously, he said, "We hunt the toktu today. I heard a wolf last night and wolves go where there are deer. We have far to go. I will harness the dogs while you get ready."

Alea dressed with an inward feeling of excitement at the thought of finding the caribou. She ate some nepko and took a drink of cold water. Then she carried out the sleeping bags and loaded them onto the sled.

It was not until late that evening that they found the deer tracks. Koopah stopped the dogs and, feeling the snow with his fingers, closely examined the footprints.

"We will not see them today," he said. "They passed yesterday, because the snow is hard inside the tracks. The deer must be over behind that mountain. It gets late. We will camp here and hunt them tomorrow.

They built an igloo, as they had done the night before, fed the dogs and then spread their bedding for the night's rest. They talked and joked and laughed long after they were snug in their sleeping bags. Alea was happy. Palliseer and all her fears of him seemed unreal and far away. When her breathing came in the regular sounds of sleep, Koopah's eyes were soft and warm as he looked over at his sister. He remembered his mother's words as she stood on the shore and said, "Koopah, take care of Alea."

It was not hard to take care of Alea. He liked to see her

happy, and to please her was always a joy to him. Koopah's brow wrinkled as he remembered that day on the hillside when Alea had screamed for him. She had been trembling and frightened, yet she had never told him what had scared her so much. She was always full of courage, even the time when she was caught in a great snowslide and nearly killed. She had made little of her danger and had laughed at Ahpea's and Koopah's concern.

Another time when she had come face to face with a polar bear, she had been wise and had remained still while the animal looked her over. No, Alea had not attempted to run away, which might have made the bear angry. She had waited for the bear to satisfy itself that she was not an enemy and had watched it shuffle off about its business without another look at her.

There was certainly something besides physical danger that now and then put that look in her eyes, Koopah decided, as on the morning they left to come on this trip. She must have been crying the night before. Why? Why didn't she tell him about it? There was no answer to his silent questionings, so, making himself more comfortable, he drifted off to sleep.

It was the afternoon of the next day that Koopah came down the hill to tell Alea, who waited by the sled, that he had sighted the deer.

"They are back of that hill. We must leave the dogs here. Take your rifle and go around that point. I will go from this side and drive them toward you. We both might get a shot as they go up the valley."

They went in opposite directions. Alea saw the caribou

feeding down on the plain. They were too far off for a rifle, so she quietly waited, her gun loaded and ready. She could not get closer without exposing herself. Her heart was beating fast with excitement and suspense and she hoped her aim would not be unsteady.

Bang! Bang!

Koopah's shots rang out. A deer reared on its hind legs and snorted with pain as it joined the others in a stampede down the valley. When they came near enough, Alea took aim at the wounded animal and pulled the trigger. It dropped and lay still while the rest of the herd made the ground shake as they thundered on past to make their escape.

Koopah came running up to Alea standing by the fallen deer.

"Oo-ee!" he called joyfully. "You killed the wounded one that was getting away. We have a fine toktu to take home. Oo-ee!"

Alea clapped her hands and danced about excitedly as she said, "We will have some good marrow to eat with the nepko tonight, and when we get home Atata will make me a new trout spear from the deer's horns."

"Go and get the dogs and sled. I will take off the skin before it freezes," Koopah said. "I must work fast or it will be frozen too hard to remove."

Alea was back soon with the team and assisted in skinning and cutting up the big animal. Sometimes their fingers got so cold they had to tuck them inside the warm skin to keep them from freezing while they cut up the meat.

They gave the liver to the dogs and watched them devour it ravenously; then fed them fresh meat until the dogs could hold no more and lay down contentedly.

While it had taken Koopah and Alea three days to get to the caribou's feeding ground, it took them four days to go back. They traveled slowly because the load was heavy and the dogs not as fresh as when they started.

Ahpea and Palliseer were out hunting when Koopah and Alea arrived home. Selalu came out and exclaimed with delight at the huge horns protruding from beneath the load.

"You bring home the toktu," she cried, and set to work helping to unload the sled. "Selalu needs the sinew from the toktu's back to use for thread to sew our boots. I hope you saved it," she said.

"We saved the sinew," Alea answered, happy at Selalu's joy over the result of their hunting trip.

Upon his return, Ahpea, too, was pleased to see the hunters and said, "I am glad you did not stay longer. That is bad country when the mild weather comes. The wind blows warm tonight. We are going to see a change. The deer hunting country has high mountains and there is much danger from snowslides. It is good you are home and with that fine meat."

Koopah talked of their hunting trip and Alea laughed at his jokes. This night there was happiness in Ahpea's house and peace in their hearts.

11

THE RESCUE

NOW TIRESOME DAYS came for the hunters. The snow melted and slush and wet made walking difficult. Selalu and Alea were kept busy drying boots and keeping them in repair. They worked ceaselessly, often staying up late at night to complete their work long after the others had gone to bed.

One morning they came out to find the air warm and sultry. They saw the rivers burst and the water come rushing down, tossing rocks and ice high into the air with a sound like thunder and with a force that made the ground tremble.

Ahpea shrugged his shoulders and said, "That is over. Next, the bay ice will break up and we will have open water. Already the surface is getting dark in patches, which means it is becoming unsafe. This will likely be the last day we hunt the seals on the ice. We had better go out at once."

Koopah said, "I will go bring home my fox traps and

put them away for next year," and he departed for the hillside and his traps.

Alea watched her father and Palliseer get ready for the seal hunt out on the bay. She assisted in harnessing and fastening the dogs to the sled. The dogs raced off, pulling the sled with the two men riding. It amused Alea to see Okpek, the lead dog, prancing as she ran, looking back at the other dogs and giving short yelps of invitation to the team to race her.

Suddenly the dogs spread out and showed fear, sensing danger even before the ice cracked. Alea gave a gasp of horror as the sled went through the ice with the two men still sitting on it.

She heard her father shout, "Hold fast to the sled, Palliseer! Don't let go!"

But even as Ahpea spoke, Palliseer made a mad leap for the ice and ran a few steps before he fell through. Only his head showed as he struggled in the water.

"Hold on! Don't let go!" Ahpea shouted as he urged the dogs to pull the heavy sled up onto the firmer ice. They tugged and pulled and the sled rose and came up on top with Ahpea still sitting on it.

He stood up and looked for Palliseer. There he was, clinging desperately to the ice and screaming for help. Ahpea saw that he himself could not get to the man without falling through. He would have to go ashore first and pull a boat out over the bad ice. But could Palliseer hold on that long?

Ahpea glanced toward the shore and his heart seemed to stop, for there was Alea pushing herself out over the ice, kneeling on her small sled. She was shoving and picking her way over the firmer patches, zig-zagging out to the man in the water.

"Go back, Alea! Go back!" Ahpea shouted in great alarm. "You will fall through! Go back!"

As she slowly pushed onward, Alea was not aware that for the first time in her life she was utterly unmindful of her father's words. Twice she saw Palliseer's head go under water; then he was in sight again, clinging to the ice. It did not matter now that he was the man she feared and disliked. She only knew she must do her best to save his life. She stopped where the white ice ended, for she knew this was as near as she dared go.

Holding up the coil of rope, she shouted, "Catch the rope and I will pull you out."

Swiftly tying one end of the rope around her waist, she threw the rope toward Palliseer. When he had caught it, she hurled herself back on the ice. Grasping the rope tightly, Palliseer slowly pulled himself up, only to fall back again. As he did so, it seemed to Alea that the line was cutting her waist in two. Desperately, she braced her feet against a lump of ice.

"Roll when you get out. Don't stand up!" she cried, as she saw him coming up for the third time.

Palliseer was exhausted and nearly dead in the cold water. His breathing was coming unevenly. At last he rolled and crawled until he lay on the firm ice at Alea's feet. The water was running from his mouth as well as his clothes and he was only half conscious.

In petrified silence, Ahpea had stood watching the rescue. "I'm going to haul the boat out and bring you both in. Don't move from where you are," he shouted as he started the team homeward.

He was back soon with the boat on the sled. Together he and Alea helped Palliseer get in and started the dogs for the shore. Selalu had seen all that had taken place. Running to meet them, she helped carry the half-drowned man into the house. After she had removed his wet clothes and got him into bed, she went outside to Alea, who was still standing by the boat.

"You were brave, Alea. You risked your life to save Palliseer. Selalu did not see you until it was too late to stop you. You might have fallen through that thin ice and drowned," she said earnestly.

"If he had done as Atata told him, he would not have been in the water," Alea answered, all her feelings of dislike for Palliseer returning now that he was safe.

Selalu's eyes were thoughtful as she said quietly, "You do not like my man."

Alea was frank in her answer. "I do not like Palliseer."

Then, seeing pain in the woman's kind face, she put her arms about Selalu and said, "Oh, but Alea loves Selalu," adding teasingly, "Palliseer looked like a wet seal down in the bottom of the boat."

They were both laughing as they walked back to the house, where they were greeted with a complaint from Palliseer, who said peevishly, "I'm about dead and you two laugh."

They looked at him seriously for a moment, but he made such a comical figure, peering at them from his sleeping bag with his hair still wet and his eyes so belligerent, that they both burst out laughing again.

Alea said to Selalu, "Now doesn't he look like a seal?"

Selalu laughed until she held her sides, for he truly did look like a seal. Then she gathered up his wet clothes and carried them outside to hang them up to dry.

As Alea turned to follow her, Palliseer called her name. The girl hesitated. She wanted no words with him, but he called her again. After all, Alea thought, he was still ill from being in the water.

"Alea, you saved Palliseer from the water," said the man. "Indian man will never be a bad man any more. I will never harm Koopah or Ahpea like I said and will never steal again."

She listened to what he had to say, then, without answering, she turned to go.

But still more was on Palliseer's mind. "Why didn't you let me drown?" he asked.

"It was like I told Selalu. I thought it was an old wet seal."

Alea giggled and, looking at the man who was still shivering, wondered why she had ever been so scared of him. She knew she would never be afraid of him again. She still disliked him, but all fear of him was gone. She would let him keep his shameful secret about the fox and the cartridges. She would not tell. He was Selalu's man and it would grieve her friend deeply to know. So, with a slight smile she left the room and went to find her father.

Ahpea looked up as his daughter came to him and he said, "I was much afraid for you when I saw you out on that bad ice. Palliseer would have drowned if you had not saved him. I could not have gotten to him in time. You were brave, my daughter."

Alea put her hand on the head of the dog that had led the team that day and caressed it fondly. "You were happy for a run today," she said to her pet. "Now the ice will go and you will grow lazy and fat. Come, I will run with you." And she raced off with the dog at her side.

That night on his way to bed, Ahpea paused outside Alea's curtain and listened to her soft breathing as she slept. Reaching inside, he tucked the blankets around her. His face was serene as he left her and went to his rest. He was full of thankfulness that this day had ended with all of them safe from what had so nearly been tragedy for one of his household. It had been a strenuous time.

12

AHPEA'S DECISION

SUMMER CAME AGAIN and Ahpea's boat once more made its way to the trading post. The going was no longer so difficult when the wind died down and they could not use the sail, for he had the Palliseers to help with the rowing, and, too, he could call on Koopah and Alea.

When Ahpea's party arrived, the traders' supply ship from England was in the harbor and the trading of skins for trinkets was already going on between the sailors and the trappers. Then and there, Ahpea decided he could no longer put off taking Alea to London, the land of the ship. His daughter must learn to read and write, to be like Tamanna, who was always boasting that she knew the meaning of writings which made no sense to Alea, but to her, Tamanna, were real words.

For a long time, Ahpea had been quietly making ready for the trip across the ocean. He had put aside money, bit by bit, until he had achieved the amount Jamieson said he should have. Saying nothing about it to Koopah and Alea, he had talked over his plan not only with the Jamiesons but with other parents who had sent their young people to London, to learn reading and writing. Yes, he was ready.

There were loud protests, that night, from both Koopah and Alea when he told them of his decision, with Alea much the louder and more vehement. "I don't want to go away on the ship," she declared.

Ahpea smiled as he saw her stormy face and said, "But it is for you, my Alea. You must learn to read and write, and you cannot learn it here."

"Why must I learn that?" Alea asked rebelliously. "I can make good boots. I can set traps and hunt seals. I don't want to read or write." Then she looked keenly at her father and with her head tipped to one side, asked, "Is it that my father thinks I do not have good sense that I must go far away to get my head fixed?"

Ahpea laughed. "Alea, you do have good sense but there is more that you must know."

Before their father could explain further, Koopah interrupted, "Yes, Alea must go and get fixed so she can shoot the seal."

"You need to go and get fixed, too," Alea retorted. "You wounded the deer that time and I had to shoot it for you."

Ahpea laughed at the heated argument, but would not be swayed from his plan. In the end, as he had known would happen, he won his point. It was agreed between the three of them that Koopah would go back up the bay with the Palliseers for company, and that Ahpea would take Alea to London.

There were no special preparations to make. They would wear their Eskimo clothes on the boat. "And when you get to London, you will at once buy English clothes for the time you are there," Mrs. Jamieson told them.

The necessary arrangements for their accommodations on the trading ship were quickly made with the Captain, who always welcomed Eskimo passengers. In no time at all, it seemed, sailing day had come.

Alea felt numb. When she boarded the ship, her eyes were red from crying. The thought of being away from Koopah all winter, of not going on trips with him, was breaking her heart. This was her father's plan, not hers. It was what he wished her to do, and so she was going.

Accustomed though she was to being out on the water in small boats, there was something about the motion of the trading ship that made her seasick for the first part of the trip. When she finally went on deck, the sky was a beautiful deep blue. White fleecy clouds made soft pillows against the blue background. It was all so peaceful that Alea drew a deep breath of happiness for the first time since they sailed. The happy moment was short-lived. The ship rolled from side to side. Looking down at the sea, seeing the waves breaking into foam and spray, she felt that nothing was peaceful, not even her stomach!

Suddenly Alea saw a black object leap out of the water, astern. Then another, and another. Oh, there were several somethings coming along behind the ship, leaping, jumping up and down. With a rush, she went in search of her father, whom she found looking out over the rail on the other side of the ship.

"Come quickly!" she cried excitedly. "I see something!"

Ahpea, delighted in Alea's first show of animation since they had sailed, swiftly followed her to the stern of the ship. Till now, this rebellious daughter of his had been nothing but a bundle of abject misery.

"Look!" cried Alea, pointing. "There, see?"

Ahpea smiled. "Those are porpoises, my dear," he said. "They enjoy following ships. They are like white whales, only smaller and black."

"Like white whales? Then they are good to eat?" Alea asked.

"We would eat them, Alea," replied Ahpea, "but I don't think the sailors here on the ship would. They think we are queer people because we eat white whales and seals and things like that."

Alea wrinkled her nose in disgust and said, "I think *they* are queer because they like pea soup and salt pork. Oh, ooh!" And running to the rail, she leaned over, nauseated afresh at the thought of fat salt pork.

Ahpea could not restrain a smile at the sight of Alea's discomfort. But quickly hiding his amusement, he led her to a chair by the bridge. "Just sit here, my daughter," he said tenderly, "and think of the porpoises. Never mind the salt pork and the pea soup."

As day followed day on the long passage to England, the trading ship encountered no severe storms, and Alea recovered from her seasickness. The Captain and the crew were very kind to the two who were their only passengers, chatting with them and describing the sights that awaited them in London. And they helped both father and daughter with their English, so that by the time they reached land they could manage the language well enough.

As the ship neared its destination, the Captain took Ahpea aside and asked, "Do you know where you are going to stay in London?"

"Yes," replied Ahpea, taking a card from his money bag. "Here is the place. Jamieson wrote it down for me, and said we would be welcome there."

Glancing at the card, the Captain nodded. "I know it well. Yes, you and your daughter will be very welcome."

Then he went on, "Since you have not before been in London, will it not be a good plan for one of my men to guide you to this place, when we land? I shall be glad to have him do so, if you wish."

Ahpea smiled in gratitude. He had said nothing to Alea of his dread of the unknown ways with which they would soon be confronted, nor of his bewilderment about what to do first. Now all was solved by this kindness of the Captain.

"You are good," he said. "And I thank you. We shall most gladly have one of your men guide us to this place."

It was night when the ship docked and Alea was asleep. She still felt numb about Ahpea's plan. It did not really matter to her when she got to where they were going. It would not be home. Returning to Koopah was more important by far than learning to read and write.

But when she awoke and dressed and went up on deck, amazement startled her from her indifference. In astonishment she gaped at sight of the buildings, all with windows, and at the boats and ships on every side there in the harbor.

Water and shore alike were scenes of lively animation. Everyone was hurrying, on land and on ship. There was bustle everywhere.

Looking at the girls and women in the crowd on the shore, for the first time in her life Alea felt self-conscious about her Eskimo dress. Glancing down at her skin boots, she compared them with the boots of these strangers. Could she ever learn to walk in such as they? And her sealskin trousers and her short coat! That coat was neat, to be sure, but there wasn't a woman or girl to be seen with one like it. As for the trousers—only men, apparently, wore those. A feeling of panic swept over her. Everyone they met would stare at her! She would be thought queer.

Ahpea, at her side, sensed the reason for her panic, and quickly said, "Remember what Mrs. Jamieson told us, my daughter. As soon as we are settled at our new place, we shall go to the store and buy English clothes."

Alea was not comforted. "Me look like that!" she exclaimed. "With boots like that?"

Then, swiftly, her sense of humor came to her rescue. "Alea will look funny," she declared with a laugh. And Ahpea felt relieved. At least, she would not be sad when they went ashore.

After they had breakfasted aboard the ship, and had said goodbye to the Captain and their other new friends, the appointed crew member got a carriage and together the three rode to the address Jamieson had given them. Alea felt terrified of the horse that started off with a sudden jerk. She knew she had never seen so fearsome-looking an animal. It was safer with the wolves up the bay than with this creature! But she said nothing of her fear, instead sitting silently and tensely, with clenched hands. Ahpea, beside her, showed no fear as he turned his head this way and that, taking in the sights and listening to what their sailor friend told them about London, as they rode along.

In a short while, the carriage came to a stop at the address on Ahpea's card. When the door was opened, it was as the Captain had said it would be. Mrs. Matson, who ran the boarding house, welcomed them cordially, and showed them to two comfortable connecting rooms, of which the sailor heartily approved. Wishing them a pleasant stay in London, he took his departure, and Ahpea and Alea were alone in their new quarters. Shortly a trim little maid came in with towels. Although she made no comment, she looked with much curiosity at Alea's clothes.

Ahpea noticed her curious glances. "Where is a store," he asked her at once in slow and careful English. "We wish new clothes."

"Wait a minute," the maid told them, hurrying away and returning shortly with Mrs. Matson.

Mrs. Matson nodded understandingly as Ahpea repeated his question. "That is always the first thing our Eskimo guests do," she answered reassuringly. "The store is not far away where you will be able to buy all that you need. Anne, here, will guide you to it."

Under Anne's guidance, they soon reached the store, where the maid bade them farewell. "You will be all right, by yourselves," she said. "The salespeople will help you."

She was right. No sooner had they stepped inside than a kind man came up to help them. When Ahpea haltingly explained their needs, he nodded and smilingly said, "Come this way."

With a saleswoman's help, Alea picked out a gingham dress and a blouse and black skirt. When she tried them on, the skirts tickled her legs. And when she looked at herself in the mirror, she burst out laughing. Again Ahpea sighed in relief. This was better than rebellion.

Matters did not go smoothly, however, when it came to a hat and shoes. Alea positively would not wear "that thing" on her head. And she turned her back when Ahpea told the saleswoman they would take it. Then the shoes! Actually, they were low-heeled, comfortable oxfords, but although the clerk declared the size was right, Alea protested that they were tight and hard and hurt. Ahpea put his hand out and turned Alea's face up to his as he said kindly, "Alea, we don't want people staring at us because we look queer. These are the kind of boots we must wear here. Won't you try to like them?"

And Alea subsided, saying nothing as her father bought underclothes and other items for her, and a suit, hat, shoes and accessories for himself. Stonily, she went to the dressing room to take off her Eskimo clothes and put on the new English ones, including the shoes.

Out on the street once more, with their old clothes in neat packages under their arms, they were no longer the object of curious glances from passersby. "See, my daughter," Ahpea said happily, "we look like all these others now. It won't be so bad when we become used to these strange clothes."

Alea glanced at her father's relieved face. He was doing this for her, even though it was not what she wished. And she loved him. He was her dear Atata. In that moment, she resolved to do just as *he* wished, as long as they stayed in London.

"I shall never care for shoes such as these," she said to him softly, as she walked gingerly along. "Skin boots are much better, and much prettier, too. But I suppose we must look like these others."

13

ALEA LEARNS TO READ AND WRITE

NEXT DAY, Ahpea told Mrs. Matson of his wish to go with Alea in search of a place where she could learn to read and write. Mrs. Matson suggested that instead of going to the lady about whom Jamieson had told them, and whose address Ahpea had on a card, they try a nearby school.

"If they will take Alea there," she told him, "it will be much easier for you." Then, going to the window and pointing down the street she added, "See, that is the place. Go there first."

Alea still felt no interest in the plans for her education. Only her great love for her father made her get ready to go out that morning. She decided on the new gingham dress and she wound her long braided black hair around her head. This was very becoming to her small face, and gave her a mature look. But by the time they reached the street, she was bare-headed, for despite her resolve to do as Atata wished, she could not stand that hat! So, as they hastened down the walk and Ahpea was intent upon their mission, she snatched the hated object from her head and hung it on the gate-post. Later, Anne saw it there and rescued it, taking it back to Alea's room.

When Ahpea and Alea arrived at the school, it was early and no one was about. Entering timidly, they were standing inside the door in bewilderment, when a young teacher came along the corridor. "May I help you?" she asked.

"Yes," said Ahpea. "I want my daughter to learn to read and write here. We are from across the sea."

"You mean she is to be a pupil in our school," the young woman asked in surprise as she glanced at Alea standing quietly beside her father.

Ahpea did not know what the word "pupil" meant, but he felt sure that this smiling young person meant to ask if Alea wished to stay.

"Yes," he said.

"But this school is for young children," the teacher told them. "For beginners. For small children, only so high," and she held out her palms a short distance from the floor.

"My daughter, Alea, is a beginner," replied Ahpea.

"I see," said the teacher. "Well, come with me."

She led them to the principal's office, and opening the door, announced, "Here are visitors from across the ocean, Miss Furness. The girl wishes to learn to read and write. Can we help them?"

Ahpea felt puzzled. He could not understand the delay. Was Alea not to be accepted for some reason? He had expected that his daughter would at once be given a book with which to start her learning. So he looked at the smiling principal in great puzzlement, as he explained his wish in his halting English. They were Eskimos from Labrador. There were no schools at home where his daughter could go. Some young people back home who had learned to read and write had come to London. So he was here, with his daughter, Alea. Could she stay and start upon her learning that very morning?

Graciously, then, the lady told him, "We cannot take your daughter into our school. It is for very small beginners. See—" and crossing the room, she opened the door upon an arriving crowd of five- and six-year-olds. Coming back to her chair, she went on, "Your daughter is a grown woman. She must be taught differently, for she is an older person even though a reading and writing beginner. She would not be happy among my children. Besides, it would not be good for her."

Ahpea looked ruefully at Alea, sitting there in her chair, and although he wondered what had become of her hat, he also knew that what the principal had said was true. She was a young woman now, and she came up to his shoulder. Moreover, she was a very attractive young woman, with her black expressive eyes that sparkled with mischief when she was in the mood. She was very solemn now, to be sure, but as soon as they found the right place for her to study, those eyes would sparkle once more.

Just then, the solemnity in Alea's eyes vanished, and wonder of wonders, the sparkles returned. "Come on, Atata," she said joyfully. "Let us go home—back up the bay. They do not want me here."

Ahpea shook his head. "No, Alea," he told her firmly, "you are going to learn to read and write."

"I'm all right as I am," insisted Alea. "I don't like it here. Come, let us go home."

"I know just the right woman to help your daughter," the principal now said to Ahpea.

At her words, Ahpea remembered the card on which Jamieson had written the name and address of the woman who had taught other foreign young people to read and write.

Taking it out and handing it to the principal, he watched her quick smile as she read what Jamieson had written. "Why, this is the very woman to whom I thought to send you—Miss Palmer," she said. "Yes, she is just right for your daughter. Many foreign-born people go to her to be tutored. Where did you get this card?"

After Ahpea had explained about Jamieson, the principal stood up and Ahpea knew the interview was over. Thanking her for her kindness, he went out with Alea to find a cab to take them to see the Miss Palmer whose name was on the card.

When they arrived at the house, they were admitted by a tall woman who introduced herself as Miss Palmer. Ahpea at once explained his wish for Alea.

Leading the way into what seemed to Alea to be an immense room filled with incredible furniture and innumerable small objects, Miss Palmer bade them be seated. Then she asked Ahpea about their home and how it had happened that they had come to England. As Ahpea slowly told her their story, Miss Palmer glanced at Alea's downcast face. Could this attractive young Eskimo girl speak English, she wondered. But she did not inquire, for she did not wish to embarrass her. Often she had to teach spoken English to those who came to her, as well as reading and writing. Well, she would find out later. Now she must make arrangements with the father. Ahpea eagerly fell in with her suggestion that she come to their boarding house for Alea's lessons, and ten o'clock the following morning was settled upon for the first one.

"I am glad to have you for my new friend," Miss Palmer said to Alea as the two rose to go. Then, taking the girl's hand in hers, she pressed it warmly.

"Thank you," Alea said, with a faint smile.

Miss Palmer was delighted. She was lovely, this girl, and evidently she already knew some English, which would be a start, at least.

The next morning, when from the front window Alea saw Miss Palmer coming up the walk, she went to the door and opened it in welcome. Already she liked this tall woman with the graying hair, who was so quick in all her movements. Although Miss Palmer's face had a serious expression, her eyes were kind and understanding.

Up in Alea's room, Miss Palmer wasted no time in taking a book from her bag and opening it to the alphabet.

"These are letters, Alea," she said, pointing to the page. "Do you know what I say?"

Alea nodded.

"Splendid," Miss Palmer told her.

Ahpea tiptoed from the room. It would be better for

him not to be there during the lessons, he decided. He would take a walk.

Despite her longing for home, Alea found that as the days passed, she actually enjoyed her lessons. She liked Miss Palmer more and more all the time, and it was not long before copying the letters on paper seemed fun to her. She could scarcely wait after each lesson to show her father what she had learned that day. Soon she was able to write short words. Often they laughed heartily when Ahpea asked the meaning of the words on the paper and Alea would have to admit that she did not know. But in a little while the words began to make sense to her, and Miss Palmer was well pleased.

When, however, the teacher introduced Alea to arithmetic, the girl's interest failed. At first she made a genuine effort to learn adding and subtracting, but the problems continued to seem senseless to her. And she came to hate the sight of those figures.

One day, laying down her pencil, she said, "If I see two seals, I say I see two seals. What use is it to say it on paper when there are no seals there?"

So Miss Palmer set aside the arithmetic and concentrated upon Alea's spoken and written English, and upon her reading. She was very proud of her pupil's progress. Alea had a keen, retentive mind, and if at times there was a far-away look in her eyes, the teacher could bring her quickly back with an amusing little story. Alea's sense of humor was a delight.

So it was that the winter days, as they passed, held more of interest for Alea than for her father. Ahpea had many moments of loneliness, often working at wood-carving with his small pocket knife, alone in his room. When that became monotonous, he still did not enjoy going outdoors. He disliked the days when London was wrapped in fog, and when he went outside he shivered in his store-bought clothes. How he wished he could wear his own warm skin suit! But people here did not dress like that and he had no wish to be stared at. Sometimes he quickly returned to his room, to watch the raindrops run down the windowpane. There was no companionship for him with the other men and the women in the boarding house, for although they were unfailingly kind to both him and Alea, they talked much too rapidly for him to grasp what they were saying. Yes, he sorely missed his Northland life, and Koopah. Dear, dear Koopah.

At Mrs. Matson's suggestion, and now and then in her company, Alea and Ahpea went to see some of the famous sights of London. But since they knew nothing of English history, the expeditions meant little more to them than a change from the boarding house. They enjoyed the docks more, where it was fascinating to them both to see the ships loading cargo for foreign ports. And always on Sunday they went to church. Alea loved the music and the singing, learning the tunes and the words quickly. Ahpea felt glad when he heard her sweet young voice joining in the hymns.

Alea's favorite hymn was "Holy, Holy, Holy, Lord God Almighty, Early in the morning our song shall rise to Thee." As she sang, Alea would slip her hand in her father's and motion for him to join in the singing. Then, as

Ahpea's voice rose with hers, they were two happy people singing to and for each other.

When at last spring came, Ahpea would hire a cab on the days when Alea had no lessons and ask the driver to take them to some park. There they would spend the day, away from the noise and clatter of the city. Often they sat for long hours while Ahpea smoked his pipe and Alea studied. At times a wistful expression would cross Ahpea's face as he looked at Alea, bent over her books. The girl in boy's clothes, hunting seals or racing over the ice as she cracked her whip to speed the dog team, seemed far removed from this young woman beside him.

They seldom talked of the home up the bay, for that made them homesick. But often they spoke of Koopah, wishing he could have seen this or that here in London, and of how he would have laughed if he could have been with them. They did not worry that they had not heard from him since they left the post, for they knew they could get no news from Labrador until the ship made its annual trip and returned to London.

Home seemed far, far away. When would they return? Would it be on the ship's next trip back? Alea hoped and prayed that it would. Ahpea could not make up his mind. Had Alea learned as much as she should? It was a question forever in his mind.

14

THE PARTY

As summer approached, Miss Palmer decided the time had come to give a party for her students, in her home. She had first thought of doing so some time before, but had decided to wait until all of them, including Alea, could speak English readily.

When the teacher broached her plan to Ahpea and Alea, Ahpea was delighted. Meeting other young people would be just the thing for Alea, he declared. Alea was not so sure. In all her London days, she had felt no slightest wish to get acquainted with anyone she met on the street. It would be a relief, she felt, if Miss Palmer would forget about the plan.

But Miss Palmer did not forget. One morning she said, "My party is to be next week. This afternoon, you and I will go to buy a party dress for you. Your father has given me the money for it, and for pumps, too."

At the store, a blue silk dress with fluffy white ruffles at the neck and around the short sleeves took Miss Palmer's eye. "Try that one on, Alea," she said. "I think it will be very becoming."

When Alea, arrayed in the blue dress, looked at herself in the mirror, she said, "I like it very much."

So the purchase of the dress was easy. But when it came to buying pumps, just as when Alea bought her first shoes, trouble arose. Alea was sure she could never walk on such high heels. But when Miss Palmer insisted upon them, she yielded.

The evening of the party, Anne offered to help Alea get dressed. She liked the Eskimo girl and was determined that she look as pretty as anyone else. When Alea had braided her long hair and wound it around her head, Anne pinned it firmly in place. Then she slipped the blue dress over Alea's head and hooked it up. Standing back to look at the effect, Anne noted with approval the lovely color with which Alea's cheeks glowed. She admired, too, the girl's full red lips, and her eyes so bright with fire and life. There was an extra sparkle in those eyes now, for this was Alea's first English party. Forgotten, for the moment, were the hesitation and the shyness that still beset her, upon occasion.

Yes, Alea was well pleased with the girl she saw in the mirror. The blue dress made her feel proud. It was so pretty. Gently she touched the lace with her fingers.

"Now for the pumps," said Anne.

When Alea had put on the pumps and stood up, she laughed to see how tall they made her. But how strange they felt, too. How could she ever walk in them? And into her mind flashed longing thought of her skin boots—

and even of the oxfords she had been wearing every day in London. Haltingly, she tried walking.

"No, wait," said Anne. "Look at me. This is the way. Don't take such long steps."

With a little practice, Alea improved, and then Ahpea was at the door saying it was time for her to leave. As Alea stood before him, tall in the new pumps, her father's eyes were happy. How lovely she looked! He was proud, indeed.

"The cab in front will take you to Miss Palmer's," he said. "I will come for you. Be happy tonight, my Alea."

Miss Palmer opened the door to Alea, and happily welcomed her. "Hang your coat in this closet here," she said, "and come right in to meet the rest of the young people."

Alea was dazzled by the lights in the room to which Miss Palmer led her. It was the one where she and Ahpea had been received, their second day in London, but it looked very different. Now, with the big chandelier aglow, it was a grand sight.

Alea followed her hostess toward the many young people who were talking together. They made so much noise, they reminded Alea of sea gulls.

Just as she was about to introduce Alea to the other guests, Miss Palmer was called away. "Wait right here," she said, "I won't be more than a minute, and I wish to be the one to make you acquainted."

With the others absorbed in their conversation, Alea was left alone. Quietly she walked to a chair and sat down. Suddenly, shyness engulfed her. She had an overwhelming desire to run away and hide from all these strange people. But she couldn't do that. It would disappoint Miss Palmer and her father.

When, at length, Miss Palmer, who had been delayed more than anticipated, introduced Alea to everyone, Alea still felt shy but with the shyness was realization of the friendliness surging around her. Everyone seemed glad to meet her, and welcomed her cordially. When they all started to play games, things were even better. There was much laughter, and Alea especially delighted in the chair game. She laughed heartily when one young man sat down heavily on the floor in his haste to get a chair.

Later, the room was cleared for dancing, and a young man sat down at the piano while a girl tuned her violin. Soon the dancers began to glide across the floor. All was motion and rhythm.

Alea did not mind that she did not know how to dance. It was a pleasure to sit there on the window seat, while Miss Palmer was away looking after the refreshments, and watch the dancing figures swirl about to the tunes the musicians played. Sometimes the dancers stopped to rest or to change partners, and Alea, almost hidden by the heavy drapes at the windows, watched in fascination.

Suddenly, swift remembrance of another dance swept over her. Then she had been dressed in boy's clothes, Koopah's clothes. But at that dance, too, she had sat and watched just as now. She glanced down at her blue dress. No, not just as now. Suddenly, homesickness, deep and silent, caught her. She wanted Koopah, her brother. She wanted her friends in Labrador. She wanted her home up the bay. Why, she was crying! A tear dropped on the hand in her lap, and another, and another. Koopah would be disgusted if he saw her crying like that. She had never done it often, not even when she was hurt.

In her distress, she drew back into the drapes and leaned against the window, which flew open with her weight. With a gasp, Alea went over the sill, landing in a flower bed below. Picking herself up, she knew she was not hurt. But she was shaken, and oh, she had crushed Miss Palmer's flowers. Now what should she do?

She looked up at the window but it was too high for her to climb through. The dancing and the music were still going on. No one had seen her fall or even missed her. Getting up, she slowly made her way around to the door. A young man, leaning on the railing of the hall stairway and watching the dancers, turned as Alea opened the door.

"Hello. You just come?" he asked.

"No, I've been here all the time," she answered. She could never have seen this young man before, of that she was certain. Why, then, was there something familiar about him?

"Been out for a walk?" the young man now asked curiously.

"No, I've been sitting on the flowers under the window," she answered in a whisper.

"On the flowers?" he repeated, thinking he was not hearing correctly.

"Yes, on the flowers. They're all mashed."

He looked so amazed that she laughed as she explained, "I fell out the window."

"Fell out the window? Are you hurt?" he asked.

"I don't think so, but the flowers are."

They both laughed.

"Why aren't you dancing?" he inquired.

"I don't know how. Why aren't you?" Alea asked.

"Oh, I can't dance as they do here. I like the way they do it at home," he said.

"Home?" she inquired.

"Yes, home at Aiviktok."

"Aiviktok, Labrador?" she asked in surprise.

"Yes. But how do you know where Aiviktok is? Nobody here ever heard of it."

"My home is up the bay from Aiviktok," she said.

He stared at her a moment, then grabbed her arm. "Alea! It is Alea, isn't it?" he gasped.

"Yes, I am Alea."

"Don't you know me? I'm Yorgke. My father sent me here two years ago, to a man tutor, with whom I have been outside of London for nearly a year. But you have grown up. I didn't know you in those clothes." He stopped abruptly. "I m-mean . . . ," he stuttered.

Alea understood. He was remembering the girl in boys' clothes whom he had asked to dance with him, and Tamanna's saying, "Be careful, she might bite you."

Alea threw back her head. "Never mind. I'm Alea and I'd rather wear trousers than this dress—rather hunt than dance—rather count deer I can see than add on paper those I don't see."

"I say, you two, come in and dance," cried a girl hurrying out into the hall.

Yorgke looked at Alea with inquiring eyes.

"I still can't dance. I just like to look," she said.

"You can't dance?" came in a surprised chorus from the other guests who had joined the girl. "Didn't you ever dance?"

"No?"

"I say . . . ," began an anemic-looking young man.

Seeing Alea's distress at the attention being paid to her inability to dance, Yorgke came to her rescue by quietly stepping forward and saying, "Friends, let me present you to the best shot and hunter of Aiviktok, Labrador. You hope some day to go big game hunting. Here's a girl who has been a big game hunter ever since she was able to lift a gun. My friend, Alea."

Alea looked silently from one guest to another. What would they say now? Would they laugh at her?

For a moment, there was amazed, disbelieving silence. Then a girl asked, "Is he joking? Are you a hunter? Can you shoot?"

Alea remained motionless as quietly and clearly she answered, "Yes, I am a hunter. I have always hunted."

Then everyone seemed to be asking questions at once as they all surged around her.

"Oh, how wonderful! Tell us about it, won't you?"

Alea smiled. "There is nothing to tell. And Yorgke is a hunter, too."

Now no one was interested in the dancing. Eagerly the young people clamored for more and yet more as Yorgke told of Arctic life—hunting, snowhouse building, and other Eskimo activities.

Alea listened with a growing feeling of homesickness. Her heart was full of love for her life back home.

Then there were cries for a story from Alea, but Miss Palmer interrupted, saying, "Let us have refreshments first. They are all ready and afterward perhaps we can persuade Alea to tell us something about her home."

Tea, cakes and sweets were served, to the great enjoyment of the guests. Judging by the number of times the food was passed around, Miss Palmer's party was already an assured success.

As her guests feasted, Miss Palmer wondered how she could put Alea sufficiently at her ease to talk about her home. There the girl was, sitting on the edge of her chair, her eyes fixed on the cup that kept slipping in the saucer she awkwardly held in her hand. Clearly, she was suffering from another attack of shyness. When that happened, Alea had difficulty speaking English.

But her guests would expect the story they had been promised, so Miss Palmer clapped her hands for attention and suggested, "Shall we go into the other room?"

They followed her into the drawing room, where she said, "Alea, won't you tell us a little about your home?"

All gathered around Alea as she stood near the window.

A girl asked, "Aren't you afraid of a gun?"

Alea, surprised at the thought of being afraid of a gun, answered readily, "No. One is safer with a gun."

"What do you do? Please tell us," the girl asked again.

"I live up the bay with my father and Koopah."

"What is Koopah?"

"My brother."

"Is he good-looking?" There was laughter at the question.

Alea answered slowly, "I never think of how he looks. He is just my Koopah, the best brother one ever had."

She was so quiet then that there were cries of, "Please go on. Tell us about him."

"Koopah is wise and kind," she said. "He always knows what to do. We go hunting together. He knows all about Big Star Hunter."

"Who is Big Star Hunter?" several voices asked at once.

Yorgke stood near by, watching interestedly. His eyes were on Alea, who now seemed unconscious of the fact that she was the center of attention. She was speaking of her beloved home and Koopah.

Drawing back the drapes, she pointed out to the sky. "Come here to the window," she said. "Look up there at the stars. Out where we live, we see them bigger and brighter. They are close to us. Here they seem far away. One star is the biggest. Koopah says it is the best one of them all. Its name is Big Star Hunter. It is always the brightest. It is never afraid of the other stars nor even the moon. They can't hurt him, so he is the happiest of all the stars. He twinkles and shines and is good to everyone. Sometimes when we go hunting and night comes, we look at Big Star Hunter and he seems to smile and say, 'It is all right; everything is fine.' Koopah says the Hunter is brightest because of the goodness inside him and because he is so wise."

As Alea told the story of Big Star Hunter, she forgot to be bashful. She was completely absorbed in her memory of Koopah and his feeling for this great, clever star. Her voice was earnest as she repeated the story of his favorite star. Her eyes shone like the stars themselves.

As she held back the dark red plush curtain, her blue dress seemed a part of the setting in the rose glow of the lights. Her head with its coronet of black braided hair made her lovely to look at. She was utterly unconscious of the picture she made.

The group looked at her admiringly, spellbound with the charm of her story and the feeling with which she told it. At last someone moved and the voices began.

"How lovely!"

"What a charming story!"

"I like that very much."

"I'd like to meet your brother. Will he come here?"

Alea smiled at the thought of Koopah's coming to London. "No, he won't come here. He is a hunter. He would not like the life here. I don't either but my father wanted me to be able to read and write, so I'm trying to learn, but I want to go home. I will ask my father to take me next ship time."

Miss Palmer explained that the ship only went to Labrador once a year. There were exclamations of, "Just imagine, living where a ship goes only once a year!"

One young man remarked with a smile, "Anyway, judging by what I see, they have very pretty girls there. Yorgke comes from that place too and he's very good-looking, but reserved and hard to know."

Miss Palmer was delighted with Alea's story and the success of the party.

Ahpea had called for Alea early and seeing that the party was still going on, had strolled into the garden. Standing in the shadows, he had seen Alea and heard her tell her story. There was no mistaking the longing in her voice. Beyond all doubt, Ahpea knew that he, too, was as homesick as she for Koopah and the home up the bay. That was where they belonged. They were a part of that which was out there—that was really living. This life was not for Alea or for him. Yes, they would go home next ship time.

Father and daughter drove to the boarding house quietly. Back in Alea's room, he put his arms around her and looked deep into her eyes.

"We are going home when the boat goes," he stated simply.

He needed no answer to tell him of her joy. Her shining eyes and happy smile were enough.

15

THE RETURN

So IT WAS that when the ship went on its next annual northern trip, Ahpea and Alea returned to Aiviktok. So it was that they came again to the trading post, eagerly searching among the few trappers who had already arrived for the sight of Koopah's face. It would have been joyous to see him when they first landed, but they were not disturbed. Koopah would come soon, and meanwhile the Jamiesons were there, eager for the story of their London adventures.

Three days after they arrived, Alea left the Jamiesons' tent early one morning. In ecstatic happiness, she looked at the beach and the shining water beyond. She again had on the trousers and coat she had worn before she left on the ship last year. The blue dress and other clothes she had bought in England were carefully put away. She spread her arms wide and breathed deeply until she felt her lungs tighten.

Suddenly her eyes widened and with a shout she was flying toward a figure that had just left a tent down the way and was walking to a boat on the shore. Without warning, she flung herself upon him, shouting, "Koopah! Koopah!"

"What's that?" he sputtered. Then seeing it was Alea, he grabbed her and they rocked back and forth as he laughed and cried, "It's Alea! You're home! You've come back! Hee-ah, hee-ah!" They were hilariously happy, both laughing and gasping in their joy at seeing each other.

Hearing the commotion, Ahpea soon joined them. They all talked so excitedly no one made sense out of what anyone else was saying.

When Ahpea declared, "Koopah, we are home to stay. We will go up the bay with you to our home," Koopah expressed his joy by lying on his back and kicking his feet in the air. Ahpea laughed. Koopah's heart was full of happiness that they were all together again.

Long they sat on the shore and talked of the past year's happenings. Koopah told of last winter. The mild weather had made hunting poor—foxes had primed late—the spring had come early. "Palliseer is a no-good hunter. He is lazy and his traps were always buried under snow or iced in. He got few skins," Koopah said.

Ahpea answered, "I think we can do without the Palliseers. Selalu is a good woman, but we have no need for her now. Alea is able to care for us and herself."

After more talk with Koopah, it was definitely decided that they would not take Palliseer with them when they went up the bay.

Ahpea glanced at Alea, who, though listening closely, had not spoken during the discussion. He was puzzled by the look of unspeakable joy that showed in her face, for he could not see why she should be so glad to leave Selalu behind. He knew Alea was very fond of the woman. He had even feared tears over the suggestion of the separation, yet here she was, absolutely radiant with silent joy. Well, she had puzzled him before and she puzzled him now. Anyway, she was happy and that satisfied him.

Three days later as Ahpea's boat made ready to leave, Selalu took Alea in her arms for a last embrace. There had been no resentment in her soft dark eyes when Ahpea told her and Palliseer they would not return with Ahpea up the bay. Now she was here early to see the family off. She waved her hand and watched the boat go out of sight. Then she slowly trudged back and entered her tent. Selalu sat down and took up her sewing, but she did not sew. Her hands lay idle in her lap. She sat lost in thought.

Those had been good years up the bay—comfortable years. She was seeing Alea coming in out of the storm, hearing her merry laughter as Selalu beat the drifted snow from the girl's clothes and they joked over the happenings of the day. Then there had been that other look on Alea's face. Selalu had seen the laughter turn to fear—dreadful fear—always, apparently, for no reason. There had never been any explanation.

Selalu's eyes were inscrutable as they rested on the still form of Palliseer dozing in his sleeping bag. He had not bothered to get up. He was not going anywhere. Why get up? Always it had been when he was near that that look had come to Alea's face and she had hurried away.

With a sigh, Selalu took up her sewing. Palliseer would

hire out to some other trapper. Without a word she would pack and go. It was always so. She would follow her man.

In the boat with her father and Koopah, Alea watched the waves run up onto the sand, leaving a wet mark as the water receded and raced back to the sea. The ocean was calm. Alea felt utter contentment. She was going home with her two loved ones. She was as serene and calm as the day itself. Ahaila, yes, life was good. All was well.

The summer passed quickly for the family up the bay. The fall came in, blustery and chilly. Then one day the rain turned to sleet, and all activity was confined indoors. That day there was no hunting.

Ahpea was filling his pipe for a comfortable smoke when Alea surprised him by asking, "Atata, will you move my bed for me?"

"Where do you want it moved?" he asked. Her bed was still by the door in his room.

"Out in my old place. Atata snores like a walrus and I want my bed where it used to be." She rubbed her face teasingly against his arm and smiled into his face.

"You wanted to sleep in there because you were lonely. Are you not lonely now, my daughter?" he asked, fondly stroking her hair.

"No, I'm not lonely now," she said with such assurance that he laughed.

"We will put your bed anywhere you want it. Come on, Koopah, pull out the nails."

When Koopah heard Alea ask to have her bed moved, he made a face of protest. "First she wants her bed in there; now she wants it out here. It's bad for the wall—it makes holes in the house taking the nails out so often. I feel a draft right now," he said, pulling his coat tightly around him in sham misery.

"If you work fast you'll get warm," Ahpea laughed, getting up to move the bed.

So the bed was put back in its former corner. Koopah was glad to see it there, but why had Alea moved it in the first place? Was it because she was lonely? No, he was sure it had not been that. Well, this change back again was for the better. Now things were as they used to be. They were all very happy. The room that had been built for the Palliseers was closed off and their home was smaller and easier to keep warm.

Ahpea had much to do after his year's absence. First he oiled his traps and got them ready for the winter. Koopah and Alea were seldom idle. Ahpea listened to their chatter and laughed at their clowning. Koopah never tired of hearing Alea tell of her year in the strange land she had visited. She showed him her clothes, with special display of the blue dress and the pumps—now always put away in her bag. He rolled with laughter when she told of falling out the window the night of the dance. That was funny—oh, ahaila, yes.

"Who do you think was there?" she asked, enjoying Koopah's laughter.

"Oh, ho, ho, I don't know," he answered, wiping his eyes, for he had laughed until the tears ran down his cheeks.

"Yorgke from near Aiviktok. He was there."

Koopah looked very surprised and said, "What did he do there?"

"He went to get some learning too," she said. "He told the guests about me, and then they all asked me to tell them a story. I don't know how I did it, but I was so lonesome I just talked about how we hunted and everything."

Koopah asked, "Don't they hunt too?"

But Alea had recounted all she would tell tonight. Now she decided on some fun, so she said, "I told them all about you."

"About me?"

"Yes. What a no-good hunter you are," she teased.

Koopah got ready for the battle. He hunched his shoulders and started to creep toward her. She dived into a corner and covered her head, laughing.

The fight was arrested by Ahpea's voice, saying, "Koopah, she did tell them about you, but with so much love and longing that we decided to come home. Alea looked fine in that dress, but the best of her was in her face when she talked of you."

Koopah decided this was no time to fight. With Alea saying nice things about him to the people over there, he'd better behave.

But then Alea said from her corner, "Yorgke was good to look at in his fine clothes. He looked as though he could beat Koopah running . . ."

With a roar the fight was on once more. Koopah chewed

and growled and they tumbled and rolled. It was good to be home again. Ahpea's heart was glad.

The fall brought little joy to the hunters of the Labrador. Often the fog was so dense that hunting was impossible. Few seals were killed. Hunger was felt over the land, and the dogs were lean. Up the bay Ahpea fared as well as any. An occasional seal and ducks feeding in the sheltered coves along shore helped them over this difficult time. Then the snows came. The sting of coming winter was in the air.

Koopah came home one evening, remarking, "I never saw so many mouse tracks as I saw today. They are everywhere!"

"I noticed them too," answered Ahpea. "Foxes live on mice. There are also many fox tracks, but when there are plenty of mice the fox is fat and not hungry for bait. I would like fewer mice and more hungry foxes."

This proved true as time passed. Every day the trappers trudged to their traps only to find them empty. The foxes paid no attention to bait, for they fattened on the small animals that were everywhere.

Then the winter struck with a severe cold that penetrated warm clothes and made the snow dry and crumbly beneath the feet of the hunters. The keen ears of the deer heard the sound and they raced away from behind hidden places before the hunters knew of their presence.

"What we need is a big fall of snow to cover the crust," Koopah said, coming in from his traps after another empty day.

"It won't snow while it stays cold like this—the air is too dry to snow. We need mild weather," Ahpea answered thoughtfully.

It was getting dark when Alea came home with the exciting report of a bear. "The Nanook, bear, made the tracks after I passed this morning!" This was news indeed.

"We won't be able to track it tonight. It will be dark soon. We will go in the morning as soon as it is light," Ahpea said, feeling a thrill of anticipation—even bears had been scarce this winter.

Alea was tired from her strenuous day of hunting and of resetting her traps, but the thought of tomorrow's bear chase kept her awake. It was a long time before she fell asleep.

At dawn they were up. The cold was brittle. The dogs shook off the snow as they rushed up to be harnessed and fastened to the sled. Alea came outside, still chewing some of the dried pepsi she had eaten for breakfast. In her deerskin suit she looked like a sturdy boy. Koopah finished putting their hunting gear on the sled and they were ready to be off.

They went in the direction Alea had gone the day before. It was not until the middle of the day that they found the tracks. Ahpea went ahead of the team and with his fingers examined the snow inside the tracks.

He came back and reported. "Those are yesterday's footprints. The snow is hard inside them. The Nanook must have gone inland to the mountain. Start the team. We will go and head off the Nanook over that way."

They started for the mountain. It was nearly evening

when at the base of Big Mountain they again found the tracks. Ahpea went ahead once more to examine the snow prints. Coming back, he said, "Nanook passed here today. The snow is soft. We must not take the dogs farther. We must be quiet. We will leave them here. Alea, you stay on this side of the mountain and watch for Nanook. It might come around that point down there. Don't try to shoot it if we are not in sight. A wounded bear is a bad bear."

The dogs smelled the scent of the animal in the tracks and softly whined in eagerness to join in the chase. Alea quieted them and made them sit still.

With their guns in their hands her father and Koopah went on to search for the bear on the other side of the mountain. She put five cartridges in the gun she carried and walked toward the point where her father had told her to watch. Under a high overhanging cliff she took her position to wait. She saw the dogs quietly watching her and knew they would make no noise to drive Nanook away.

When a shot rang out over on the other side of the mountain, she felt a thrill. She knew that her father and Koopah had found the bear. They must be enjoying the chase. She listened to the excited voices of the two men, but she could not make out the words. She heard the growls of the bear; then all was still. She hoped Nanook had not escaped.

Some time passed. Then some sand and small rocks rolled down from overhead, and Alea glanced up. There, directly above her on the cliff, staring down at her with pain-laden eyes, was the huge bear. Looking down at her, it shook the frosted blood from its jaws and roared its anger as it crouched to make a leap. Alea flung herself flat against the icy cliff. She felt the swoosh of air as the beast fell past her to land on its haunches on the hard, crusty snow.

Awkwardly it got to its feet and turned to face her for a second attack. Blood speckled the whiteness of the snow as the bear shook its head and glared balefully at her. Alea watched in petrified horror. Desperately she pointed her gun and pulled the trigger—just as the beast was making the leap. Beneath the overhanging cliff the shot was deafening and her ears stung with the roar. The animal seemed to crumble as it fell over and lay still.

Just as Alea fired, Ahpea came running up and saw the bear fall. He rushed to the girl, who still stood pressed against the cliff, the smoking gun in her hand, staring at the bear. He caught her to him.

"That was close, my daughter. You fired just in time to save your life. If you had missed, it would have killed you."

Alea, shaking with fright, was glad for the comfort of her father's nearness. She had fired almost without realizing she was doing so. Indeed, she had felt surprise when the gun went off and the bear dropped. She had not even taken aim—she had just shot in the direction of the beast.

Koopah came rushing up his face tense as he glanced at his father who still held Alea close. "I was afraid for Alea when I saw that ol' Nanook go up over the top of that mountain. I never saw anything run as fast as this one—it went up like a fox. I ran, but I had to go around the mountain, but that ol' Nanook went right up over the top!"

Ahpea said, "The Nanook was hurt and angry and meant to get away; then it saw Alea down below and blamed her for everything. Only her quickness saved her life. She threw herself against the cliff as the Nanook jumped. The weight of its body made it stumble and gave her time to shoot it. We can be grateful this day that she is safe."

Alea said, "My knees felt like water when I saw that Nanook looking at me from up there with its mouth open, as if it were already tasting how good it was to eat me. Ahaila, I was a no-good hunter that time." She smiled ruefully.

Ahpea said, "A good hunter is one who knows when to be afraid. You did the only right thing to do, my daughter, and it was you who killed Nanook. I shot it only enough to make it angry."

They skinned the bear and loaded the meat onto the sledge. After they reached home the dogs were fed good, fresh Nanook; then the dogs rolled and cleaned themselves before lying down in the shelter of the house. The rest of the meat was put out to freeze and the skin cleaned and spread out to dry.

Ahpea said, "This is the biggest Nanook skin I ever saw!"

They felt glad for this day's hunting, but while Koopah and Alea talked over the day's events, Ahpea thought about Alea's close escape from the bear. If she had missed when she fired, the beast would have been on her in another minute. Ahpea put away his work and took up his pipe for a last smoke before going to bed.

Alea's laughter rang out merrily at some remark Koopah made as he put his boots up to dry. As before, the work was shared by them all. Much to Alea's delight, Koopah always grumbled and complained about this "woman's work." She knew full well that he was glad to do his share of this work and made a fuss about it just for her benefit.

"How ugly these boots look," Koopah complained. "Look at this now. If my foot was like that I'd walk backwards." The boot certainly did look dry and twisted, but some chewing and rubbing were all that was needed to make it as good as new.

As Ahpea went to his bed that night he heard Alea's merry laughter as she continued to tease Koopah, and the sound was good to his ears. He was grateful that they were all safe at home after the terrifying experience with the bear.

Ahaila, it was good to be home. All was as it should be. Yes, Ahaila.

16

DISTURBING NEWS

WHEN SUMMER DAYS had come again, they all made ready for the trip to the trading post, a time always a joy to Alea. But on this trip, the sea was rough and sometimes it seemed the boat would never right itself as it keeled over before the brisk breeze. But it was a stout craft and obeyed the hand that steered it.

When they arrived, they found that the ship had brought disturbing news—news only vaguely understood by the people of the Labrador but which made all faces grave. The land across the waters, the ship's land, was at war. True, it was far away from here, but this was nevertheless bad news.

Alea found it hard to think of the ship's people fighting and could not understand why she felt disturbed. She did not know the meaning of her father's look that rested so often on Koopah. That evening, after they had gone into their tent for the night, so deep and grave was Ahpea's expression that the faint feeling of unrest seemed to swell up in her. They were not in the ship's country—why were people so worried? The fighting could not reach them here.

She watched her father load his pipe and light it. Then she asked, "Why do you look so, Atata? What we heard today about the great trouble in the ship's land is far from us. It won't come here. We will be up the bay."

Ahpea smoked on silently; then, taking the pipe in his hand, he said, "No, the great trouble won't come to us up the bay, but war means young men must leave home. If it goes on, all our young men may be called to go and fight. For we belong to the land of the ship."

Alea still did not fully understand the meaning of his words. "But we don't know those people who fight," she declared. "We won't go to them—we will stay up the bay!"

"Alea, it will come closer. If all young men are called, Koopah will have to go too."

"Koopah? He won't go to fight anybody." She shivered at the thought.

Surprised at what he heard, Koopah looked at his father and spoke emphatically. "Me fight somebody? No, not me. I'm not even vexed at those people!"

Ahpea smiled at Koopah. "It's war, son," he said. "The people are not angry at each other, they are just fighting . . ." He stopped trying to explain this thing. How could he tell these young people the reason for the fighting when he himself did not know it?

Ahpea had lived in this Northland all his life, except for that short trip last year. He knew as little of the cause of war as the two here watching him. He knew only that Mr.

Jamieson had said that the young men of Labrador would have to go if they were called. That was why faces were so anxious at the news the ship had brought today.

He said with a sigh, "I hope it won't last long and doesn't reach us."

Indeed, up the bay war was far from the minds of Koopah and Alea in the following months. Once in a while Ahpea thought of it and hoped it was over by now. And that was all.

Hunting was good for them that winter. Often the house was rank with the smell of drying skins. A goodly bundle of dry pelts hung from the rafters in the back room. Ahpea, Alea, and Koopah had made many trips far into the interior, for they had a fine dog team now.

Then it was spring. The ice broke up and floated loose in the bay.

"We will go to the post with a fine lot of skins when the ice clears," Ahpea remarked, proudly shaking out the white fox he had taken off the drying board. "This one is just beginning to turn dark, which means the fur will be shading soon."

The next day was spent taking up traps and storing them away. The trapping season was over for that year.

The loose ice was still blocking the bay when the three were surprised to see a boat pushing its way to their landing place. Ahpea recognized the two Eskimos who were rowing and greeted them cordially. The third man was a stranger. As he stood up to get out Ahpea knew he was from the ship's land. Some inner voice told him this was war. This was what he had tried to explain to Koopah last summer.

The stranger stepped ashore and looked at the three standing there watching him. He held out his hand and said in the Eskimo language, "You are Ahpea?"

"Yea."

Turning to Koopah, he said, "This must be the young man I've come to see."

Ahpea asked, "Has the ship already come to Aiviktok? The ice just broke up. It is early."

"The traders' ship has not come yet. But another steamer is at Aiviktok. It has come to take all able young men across the sea to help fight a war. I was sent to tell your son to report to the trading post at once. Will he come with me now or will you bring him in your own boat?"

Koopah was too surprised to speak. In silence, he stood listening, making no effort to say anything.

Alea put her arms around him and said protectingly, "No! No! Atata, Koopah is not going with that man. Make him stop talking that way."

Ahpea made a slight motion with his hand to still the storm he saw gathering in Alea's face. Quietly he told the man, "We will take Koopah to Aiviktok. We will be ready to go in the morning."

The stranger stepped back into the boat, saying, "The ship will be there for several days. There are many young fellows up the bay that I must round up, so we'll go on. Good day to you."

The boat shoved off. As it pulled out of sight the

stranger waved his hand. With a sigh he took his seat in the stern of the boat and loaded his pipe. He had done the job he had come to do. Another family had been notified. Another boy would leave home, perhaps never to return. In his mind's eye he still saw the three on the shore. The father had said little, but something had gone out of him there on the beach at the thought of his son's leaving. Ahpea would bring the young man to Aiviktok all right, but his heart would go with his son, just the same. Nice man. Oh, hang this war!

After silently watching the boat go out of sight, Koopah turned to his father. "Must we do what the man said? Go to Aiviktok now?"

"Yes, we must go. This is that war we heard of last ship time."

He looked at Koopah's troubled face. Alea was standing with the tears very near, waiting to hear what was coming next.

"We will go to see what they want us to do," Ahpea said.

"But I want to live here, up the bay with you. I want to come back here," Koopah said, completely bewildered.

Up until now, decision of when to go to the trading post had been made by the family, at the time Ahpea was ready. Now they were going because a strange man had come and in effect said, "You must." Never before had Koopah been told "you must," not even when he was little. Ahpea had always asked him to do things—not ordered him. And the stranger's words were an order.

Ahpea, seeing Koopah's perplexity, put his hand on the

strong young shoulder. His voice was deep with feeling as he looked into the face so brown and tan with the past winter's cold and wind.

"My son, you have never turned away from hard things," he said in a steady voice. "You have always gone forward to what you should do. Now you go to see what is wanted of you, and of us. I don't like it myself, but it is right for us to go."

"Yes, Atata, we must go to see what they want." The young man nodded his head in agreement and turned toward the house to get ready.

Ahpea did not follow the other two into the house. He walked slowly along the shore, deep in thought. Going up on the high point, he sat down and gazed out over the ice that grated and churned with the strong tide. Near the shore the open water looked still and calm. The gulls screeched noisily as they dived down for small fish or shells dragged up from the bottom by the moving ice.

Sitting on the rock, Ahpea looked toward the house. It seemed very peaceful and quiet. A long time ago he and Soona had built the house themselves. They had worked hard and had worn blisters on their hands cutting down the wood for the house.

A tender smile played at the corner of Ahpea's mouth as he remembered Soona holding out her hand and then looking at his blister and with her head held to one side, saying mischievously, "How did you get that good, fat blister? I got just a small, flat one. Will do better tomorrow."

Laughter and tears had come to him there. This was home. Now one more member was to leave it.

Tomorrow he would start to the post with Alea and Koopah. Koopah would not be coming back with them—maybe never. He was going to war. Ahpea stirred restlessly. Why must Koopah go away to fight?

Koopah had grown into a fine young man. It was hard to believe he was the half-dead, starved boy of that time long ago when Ahpea had found him and brought him home to Soona. Ahpea was proud of Koopah. Yes, he was a good boy. It would be lonely without him.

Ahpea got to his feet and stretched his arms high above his head. It was then that Koopah chanced to come out of the house and see his father's tall figure with its arms skyward. It was a picture he was never to forget: a lonely figure of a man reaching to the sky; a patient man who never complained, even now when events had brought to him the fact that from here on only Alea was left to him out of his family. Yes, Ahpea would go on, meeting whatever the day brought without anger or complaint.

Koopah could never remember a time when his father was hasty or impatient. He was always quiet and kind. Now the sight of Ahpea alone up there pulled at Koopah's heart.

The next day was fine with a slight off-shore wind. The skins were loaded in the boat, together with all that Koopah was to take. This was more than Alea could stand. She broke down and cried as his clothes were being packed. Even fun-loving Koopah had found little to joke about since the news came that he had to go to war. They were all unusually quiet and except for a few remarks or questions, they loaded the boat in silence.

They made the trip in good time and were surprised to see so many trappers and families at Aiviktok. Tents were pitched along the bank. Many kayaks were pulled up on the beach. Out in the harbor the ship was anchored, the smoke from its funnel making a dark blotch against the blue of the sky of this fine day.

Ahpea's boat was greeted with words of, "So, they even found your boy! We thought you'd still be iced in, in that sheltered bay."

Ahpea answered, "The ice just broke up. The off-shore wind made it clear along the shore and we were able to get out."

Plenty of willing hands helped them put up their tent. Then Ahpea and Koopah unloaded some of their things from the boat and settled the bedding for the night—all but Koopah's; that remained in the boat. Again, the sight of Koopah's belongings in a bundle made his going away very real, and Alea's face quivered as they finished getting settled before going out to the ship.

Ahpea was grave, too, as he faced his young people. This might be the last time they would be alone together for many months. Forcing a smile, he said, "Now we will go to see what they want us to do."

Alea broke into wild sobs. "They will take you away on that ship, Koopah, and we will never see you again. People will fight you," she cried.

For a moment Koopah felt he was going to break down too. He felt he could not stand to leave these two loved ones, but he saw Ahpea needed his help. Alea was crying and Ahpea always felt lost when Alea cried. Their father now looked so desolate and unhappy that, swallowing his own emotions, Koopah said with mock surprise, "They fight me? I wish they would. What fun for Koopah! Ho, ho, ho."

Then more seriously, he said, "Alea, when we got here I saw a lot of people on the shore who do not want their sons to go away. Some of them have brothers, too. You must show them you are brave. Take care of Atata and our dogs until I get back. It may not be for long." And he flung his arms around her.

Ahpea said, "That is true. Many of our friends are giving their sons and brothers too. We will wait for Koopah to come home. And you, Alea, will write your brother news of his home and of us. Jamieson will tell us how to send your letters."

Ahpea paused, cleared his throat and said in a husky voice, "Son, always be careful. Always be fair."

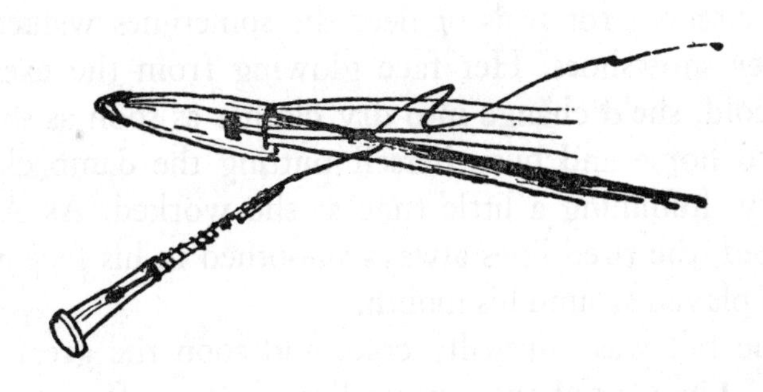

17

THE SMOKE SIGNAL

Without Koopah life up the bay was different for Alea and her father. Ahpea never had much to say and although Alea tried to overcome the stillness by chatting gaily about the day's happenings and often had her father laughing at her stories, the house was much too quiet without Koopah's fun.

Alea was never idle. Home duties often kept her from her traps. But she did all her indoor work cheerfully and willingly. When she could get out, however, she rejoiced. In her search for seals or deer she sometimes walked far on her snowshoes. Her face glowing from the exertion and cold, she'd change into dry clothes as soon as she returned home and busy herself putting the damp clothes to dry, humming a little tune as she worked. As Ahpea listened, the tired lines always smoothed in his face and a smile played around his mouth.

The fall was unusually cold, and soon the great frost came. The play of the Aurora Borealis was often magnificent, lighting the whole countryside with its brilliance.

The soft, vibrant colors contracted and expanded at the whim of the wind. People thrilled to its beauty as they looked on with upturned faces.

"Ahaila," Eskimo mothers told their children, "that is put there by the good spirit so we can find the great Nanook or hunt the toktu. It is there to help the Innuit, Eskimo people, when the great cold comes and the days are dark. Ah-huh, that is good," and the children felt no fear.

Spring followed with its melting snow. The ice thawed and its sharp, needle-like points cut into the dogs' feet as they hauled the sled. Ahpea made shoes for them by cutting wide strips of skin and tying them on securely over the dogs' ankles. This helped, but both Alea and her father laughed heartily at the way the dogs danced around the first day they wore the shoes, trying to shake them off.

The rivers burst, tossing aside the ice and rocks. The waters once more flowed toward the sea.

Then came summer with its warmth and brightness—blue skies over which fleecy clouds floated and looked like soft pillows.

Alea liked to sit on the rocks and look into the water at the foot of the overfall near their home. This had always been a favorite spot for her and Koopah, and she longed for him now and wondered where he was. She saw the salmon as they migrated to the sea from the lakes. She marveled at the shining beauty of each one as she saw them come to the edge of the overfall, pause a moment, then seem to decide on the jump that tossed them into the seething waters below, to swim swiftly on down the river.

She liked to shove the boat out on the calm water and float along, her oars resting lazily in the rowlocks. Her London days seemed like a story that had been told about someone else. This was where she belonged. What she was seeing now was more important than reading and writing. There was a pink jellyfish. She wondered if it could see. She could discover no eyes in it. Did it hurt when she hit it with the oar and it disintegrated and mixed with the water? Down in the clear water were many small fish, and on the bottom she saw the shells and starfish and the clumsy, lazy sculpins.

She got her biggest thrill later in the summer when she saw the first grampus of the season. They came up in the water, huge and black, diving and blowing steam into the air. She knew her Eskimo people never killed them. They were yearly visitors to their waters, harmless and welcome.

With the coming of the grampus, the codfish season opened. The grampus drove the fish into the shallow waters, and the Eskimo people rejoiced and got their hooks and lines ready.

Alea's boat often rode deep in the water with the weight of her catch. Her father worked with her to clean and put the fish out to dry in the sun. Together they spread the fish on the cliffs and rocks, turning them many times until they were completely dry and could be stacked away to take to the post and trade for supplies.

Some days both Alea and her father fished and spent much time in the boat and did not get their work done until very late. Alea's hands were calloused and sore from the salt water and her fishing lines, but she went out again the next day. All this belonged to the cod season.

Often her father went out in his kayak, but with the grampuses disturbing the bays the seals had gone far out to quieter waters. He got two that summer, but mostly he came home without even seeing any.

One day Ahpea decided to go up to the top of Big Lookout Mountain, back of their home, and search with his spyglass for deer. From there he could look far to the great plains. Now he looked toward the horizon and said, "If you use the boat today, don't go too far out. A storm is brewing and you might have trouble getting back. The sky looks like wind soon."

Shortly after he left, Alea went out in the boat. The sea was so still she did not expect any trouble. She fished, but sometimes she just sat and watched the sea gulls diving for the bits of cod liver she threw out to them. They were greedy birds, she thought, watching them snatch the food from each other. Sometimes they plunged down with a speed that made her think they would break their necks when they struck the water. But no, they got the food and flew off with easy grace to eat the liver in peace.

Suddenly the boat gave a lurch and she looked up to see a storm racing across the water toward her. She grabbed the oars and tried to keep the bow toward the shore, but the wind tore the boat from her control and tossed it about until she had difficulty sitting on the seat. She struggled desperately to row, but the wind whipped the boat away from the shore and rocked it crazily. She took in the oars to keep from losing them overboard. She was drenched with the spray, and the boat was half full of water. She held on and steered and tugged with all her might until she got the boat turned around, away from the rocks ashore. The boat was now drifting madly across the bay before the wind.

As she neared the farther shore, the water was not quite so rough and she was able to guide the boat to a sheltered cove around the point. The boat was nearly swamped as it grated on the sand. She hurriedly got out and pulled it in as far as she could and tied it fast. The water dripped from her clothes.

Alea stood looking down at her soaked self and grinned. If only Koopah could see her now! Then she walked up over the point to look toward her house. There it was, so peaceful and quiet, far across the bay. But there, too, between her and home, was a seething mass of angry sea-foaming waves that drifted as they broke. She wondered if her father had returned yet. He would be very alarmed for her safety when he came home and found the boat gone.

Then she became less tense as she felt in the pocket of her trousers. Yes, there it was—her flint. Later on she could make a fire and signal her father.

When she went back to the shore, the tide had gone out and the boat was high out of the water. She bailed out the water and saw the fish she had caught, swimming about and still alive. Oh, she thought, they have been having a good time in all that water, but I'm not going to keep my boat full of water just so they can swim.

For some time she looked at the lively cod; then one

by one she dropped them into the sea and watched them swim away. She kept two in case she had to stay away from home long enough to need food. Her father had taught her that this was right in the land of the Innuit, who never killed merely to destroy.

She went up on the point again and gathered dry wood. Taking a handful of dry moss, she struck the flint sharply against a piece of file and, as the sparks fell, she puffed and blew until the moss ignited and she had a blaze to put among the dry twigs.

After she had a good fire going, she slowly began drying her clothes. She could not remove them, for she had no others. The fire felt very good and after a while she was almost dry. Then, thinking her father must be home by this time, she put turf on the fire and smoke billowed skyward. She let the fire build up and then doused it. She repeated this for some time before she saw the answering signal. Her father's smoke puffed up and died down, puffed up and died down, telling her he understood she was safe and all was well.

She sat in the boat and listened to the roar of the wind. This was a sheltered spot. She built a fire on the beach to keep away any stray wolves. All through the night she dozed, getting out only to build up the fire, then getting back in the boat again. Once she felt the boat moving, and knew the tide was in and she was afloat. She was not afraid, for the boat was securely fastened to the shore and there was no danger of its drifting away. She was still there at daybreak when Ahpea's kayak came up beside her.

"Atata, how did you get across in that great storm?" she asked, surprised that he was really here.

Ahpea let his breath out and shook the spray from his face. "I was afraid you might try to cross when daylight came. You would not be able to guide the boat. I feared for you and had to come."

"The big wind came quickly," she said. "The boat filled with water. I was not able to guide it to our shore, so I steered it around that point and to this shelter."

"My daughter was in great danger. She has an old head on young shoulders, as I see by the fire that burns. We will stay here today. Tomorrow that angry sea will be getting worn out. I will be glad to rest after the hard pull I had to get here. Sometimes the sea was higher than my head and I feared it would cover me, but my kayak was light and came to the top of the waves."

Ahpea was satisfied just to be there with Alea—both of them together. He had had a bad time last night, knowing his daughter was in danger from the sea. He had risked his life to get across the bay in the great storm.

Later, hearing their laughter at Alea's account of the fish swimming in the water in her boat, when she herself looked like a drowned fish, one would not have guessed that both of them had faced death a short time earlier. They were happy and contented and when the weather eased its anger, they would go home. They ate, joked and laughed. Today was good. Yes, today was very good.

18

AHPEA'S FALL

Ahpea came home late one cold winter day with a piece of red fur in his hand. He was disgusted at having found another fine skin destroyed by the wolves.

"The wolf is hungry and gets to the trap before I do," he said. "This is all that was left of my fox."

Alea said, "All I got yesterday was the foot of a white fox. Yes, the amagok had been there first."

The next day it was the same—another fox torn up and devoured.

"The deer must be close by—the wolves follow them. If I go inland, I may find the caribou herd and we will have some good toktu to eat. I will go tomorrow," Ahpea declared.

The next night, Ahpea did not come home but Alea was not worried. She knew he would not turn back if he got on the tracks of some animal, and she hoped he had found deer.

She fed the dogs and watched them roll in the soft snow to clean themselves after their meal. Alea chuckled as her pet dog, Okpek, stuck her head down in the snow and came up sniffing and snorting with the snow up her nose.

"You are a stupid dog," Alea laughed. "You should know you will smother if you poke your head down in the deep snow."

She hugged Okpek and squealed as the dog tried to lick her face. "No! No! You smell like a seal—you must clean yourself good. Go on, you'd better roll much more in the snow. See?" She rolled herself over and over in the snow, to the dog's delight.

When Ahpea returned, he brought deer meat as well as a red fox skin. His report of the wolves was rather alarming.

"I killed this deer the evening I left home, but this is all that I was able to save. The amagok came and ate up the meat during the night. I set a trap and got this fox this morning. We must go back and try to get more. We must not take the dogs. They might get caught in the traps. It is a long walk and we must carry our sleeping bags."

Alea was delighted with this plan and gathered together the necessary things to take with them.

They were ready to start early. Alea's strong young back was bent beneath the load. Burdened as they were, they walked slowly. It was late evening when they got to Ahpea's camping place. There they set their fox traps where the blood on the snow told of a previous kill. And they built their igloo close by, lit their lamp and settled for the night. Then Ahpea put his wet mittens up to dry.

They were eating pepsi when suddenly Ahpea became tense and glanced toward the door. Sitting absolutely still,

Alea watched his face. His sense of hearing was so keen he had heard something she had missed. She saw him reach for his gun and silently slip out into the moonlight. She heard the shot and went out quickly. Her father was pulling a dead wolf nearer the house.

"I was listening for him and heard him go past the door," Ahpea told her. "I knew he would come back after it got dark. We will have a good amagok skin to trade and some more meat to feed the foxes."

Ahpea skinned the wolf and dragged the carcass down to where their traps were set, then returned to rest until morning. He was pleased that there was one less wolf to steal foxes from the traps.

Lying in his sleeping bag, Ahpea wondered where Koopah might be tonight. The young man was always in his father's thoughts. Koopah was brave and fearless. Was his courage helping him now wherever he was?

Ahpea glanced at Alea in her sleeping bag. She was sleeping peacefully. He turned over and soon his breathing, too, had the deep rhythm of a man who slept.

The next morning the traps held two foxes. The man and the girl stayed to skin the animals and reset the traps, but they caught no more.

The second morning, Ahpea said, "We must go home. Our dogs need us to protect them from the hungry amagok. They have only their teeth to fight with, and there are many wolves this year."

Again the two adjusted the straps around their bundles and bowed beneath the load. All day they tramped homeward. Their dogs greeted them with yelps of joy.

Alea said nothing as she sat watching her father put the skins on the drying boards to dry—two foxes and a wolf. But her admiration was expressed two days later when he removed them from the boards and turned the fur side out.

"Oh! Oh! Atata, that is a big amagok!"

It was indeed a beautiful skin—light gray in color and full-furred. Alea put the warm skin up to her face, then took it down quickly. "I smell amagok!" she said in faked alarm, which made Ahpea laugh.

Her father said, "I don't mind the amagok eating my deer meat now that I have this good skin."

"I wish Koopah could see this. He would be proud too," Alea said thoughtfully.

"He might be on the ship when we take this in, next summer. Then he will see it."

Ahpea watched Alea that evening as she stood at the curtains around Koopah's bed. He had seen her standing there before. She never leaned inside the curtain of the bed, simply stood at the opening looking in—just as she would have done if he were there and she needed to speak with him. Tonight, she was there a long time; then quietly she closed the curtain and went to her bed without a word.

Ahpea remembered that even as small children Koopah and Alea had respected each other's privacy, neither going beyond the other's curtain. It was an unspoken rule that had always been observed. So now she paid her silent nightly visit outside Koopah's curtain. So real to her was her brother's presence there, she could almost see his laughing face and hear his "Hee-ah! Hee-ah!"

The next day Ahpea came home from hunting along the mountain side looking drawn and breathing with difficulty.

"I slipped and dropped over a cliff," he told Alea. "My chest struck a rock. At first I could not breathe and it still hurts to take a deep breath. It will be all right after I've had rest, but it doesn't feel good now."

Ahpea lay down and Alea did the work. Before she went to bed she took care of everything for the night. She did not sleep well, for she kept hearing her father coughing and turning as though he were uncomfortable and trying to make himself more easy.

Ahpea was not able to get up the next morning and Alea stayed home with him. She fed the dogs, brought in ice and melted it for drinking, and cut wood and piled it in the wood box–enough to last a couple of days, for she knew she must go to her father's traps tomorrow if he still felt sick. She kept the house warm and waited on him. She chatted gaily, certain that her father's accident would have no serious consequences. Her father slept fitfully through the day, but she knew he had not had much rest last night. She moved about quietly, trying not to disturb him.

She dressed early the next morning and got ready to go the rounds of her father's traps. She must reset them so they would not be iced in. After her meal, she put logs in the stove to keep the house warm for her father. Then she tiptoed to his room and looked at him sleeping. She did not pull the curtain over the door, but left it open to let in the warmth. The water and food she had brought him last night was still beside his bed. He could reach it if he wanted it. He had not been hungry last night.

She spent a tiresome day on her snowshoes. The snow was deep and soft. She trudged on from one trap to another, setting and scraping the crusty ice from them. She found one fox caught by the hind foot. It was lively and she had difficulty killing it. She was glad she had this skin for Ahpea.

When she got home, she was happy to see that her father was up and in the outer room. He worked on the cleaning of the fox while she talked and told of her day's work.

"Amagok did not have time to eat this fox. It was too lively. It must have just got in the trap. It wanted to bite me." Her eyes were bright as she laughed at the memory of her tussle with the fox.

Her father did not complain of his pain, but she saw him flinch when he drew a deep breath. And she noticed, too, the dark shadows under his eyes, and his lips so strangely blue. He must have been hurt badly, but rest would cure that.

She was very happy when at last her father was able to get out and hunt again. She went to her own traps with a feeling of lightness, for now Atata was well. But when she saw how exhausted he was on his return, she realized he had been hurt worse than he would admit. The fall had done something to him. He was not well and in a few days he was again unable to leave the house.

She went back to his traps. The wolves were always on the prowl for any fox too exhausted to put up a fight. She worked hard with her father helping as much as he could, but there was little he could do. He found breathing painful and difficult.

Alea was weary at the end of each day. She chopped wood, shoveled snow that drifted and covered the door, and cared for the dogs. Then she slept soundly through the night and at daybreak she was off again, hunting and trapping. She had no need for the team, and the dogs grew fat and lazy. Yet with her father ill, she got comfort from the dogs' presence, whenever she took them with her.

19

THAT NIGHT A WOLF HOWLED

ALEA WAS BENT beneath the load she carried on her back. She had two legs of the deer she had killed that day—a young doe that had become separated from the main herd as it raced madly away from the wolves that chased it.

The night was brittle with cold. Her breath froze as she exhaled. A low drift swirled over the hard snow. Pausing a moment, she shifted the load from her shoulders and straightened up, reaching her arms upward to ease herself. She looked at the blue sky with its millions of stars. Ahaila, there was Big Star Hunter up there among all the others. She remembered Koopah's love for this particular star and whispered, "Do you see Koopah from up there? Is it for him you smile this night? Tell him I got this deer. We have fresh meat. We are all right, only Atata is hurt. He . . ."

She stopped, for she was very close to tears. Brushing her hand over her face, she picked up her load and started a fast walk toward home. She had a feeling that she needed to hurry. She was seeing her father as he had looked this morning when she went in to say goodbye before she left. He had the blue look about his mouth that she remembered seeing so often lately, and those dark shadows under his eyes. He had smiled at the look of concern on her face and said, "I won't get up today. Don't go too far, my daughter. Take care of yourself."

The dogs met her with their usual yelps and wagging tails. Placing her gun against the wall, she entered the house. The lamp gave out a dim light. The fire burned low in the stove. There was no sound from her father's room.

She removed her outer garments and changed into dry boots before going into the other room. From the doorway she saw him in his sleeping bag. She tiptoed to the bed. His face was turned away from her as he lay on his side.

Putting her hand on his shoulder, she leaned over him and spoke softly. "Atata, I'm home."

When he did not move, she lightly touched his cheek and drew her hand back with an exclamation of horror at the coldness of him. Almost roughly she drew the cover away from his face, the better to see him. She shook him, calling, "Atata! Atata!" She turned him on his back and only then did she realize he was not breathing.

"No! No! Atata, no!" She heard herself screaming and put her hand over her mouth to deaden the sound.

Unable to stand, she lowered herself to sit beside him on the bed. Utterly incapable of thought or action, she sat there as still as the one beside her. The hours went by. The night was dark and deep. Alea was not aware that the fire had gone out and the house was cold. Except for a shudder that occasionally shook her, she was conscious of nothing. She was alone with a grief too deep for tears.

In the early dawn a wolf's long-drawn-out howl broke

the night's silence. It continued until the dogs outside the house turned their noses skyward and joined in. It was her dogs' need that brought movement to Alea. She rose stiffly and went outside, dragging her feet as she walked. She quieted the dogs and let the wind bite into her face; then she returned to the house and walked aimlessly about the outer room. She must do something. There was help at Aiviktok but that was many days' travel.

Suddenly she stopped pacing the floor. There was Jamieson, her father's friend. It was to him Ahpea always turned when in trouble. That's where he would want to go now. It was far down the coast from here, but the dogs were well rested. They had not worked since her father's injury. They would take her to Jamieson's.

She wasted no time. She harnessed her dogs, then came inside to dress in her warmest deerskin suit. She packed her spare clothes into a bag, returning outside to push the long sled into the room and up to her father's bed. Long she stood and looked at him.

"Atata, we will go to Jamieson," she said softly. "He will help us. I will take you." She put her arms about him. "Atata, I will be as you told me," she sobbed.

Slowly she covered the beloved face. She did not hesitate. Her face was as white as Ahpea's, as she tugged and pulled and got the body into the sleeping bag and onto the sled. Next she loaded on her other belongings and covered the entire load with a bearskin, lashing it all on securely. Then she harnessed the dogs to the sled and started them out the door. Obediently they pulled the sled outside, then waited for her to tell them what to do next.

Alea went back into the house and put out the lamp.

There was the meat she had so proudly brought home yesterday. It seemed a long time ago. She had not eaten; she was not hungry; but the dogs soon would be. Adding the two legs of deer to the load on the sled, she carefully closed the door, and started the team.

The day was fine and the snow hard. She had never made this trip before, but she knew the Jamiesons' winter place was on the coast of some bay far off to the south. She could not miss it if she followed the shore and the weather remained fine.

Keeping to the coast was hard work, for the going was very rough. Determinedly she pulled and steered the heavy sled. Often she had to run forward to clear lines that had tangled around rocks or ice. She hurried the team on and made good time the first day. As night closed in she built a shelter. She was her father's daughter—resourceful, never faltering. She was not doing this for herself. It was for him, in his great need.

The igloo she built was not large, but it was her home while she waited for the night to pass. The snow blocks were well put together. After she got her stone lamp lighted, she went outside and built a house around and over the sled. She did not disturb the load except to fetch her sleeping bag. She unharnessed the dogs, brought in the lines, and then cut up a leg of the deer meat and fed it to the dogs. Her house was warm from the lamp, and although she did not feel hungry, she ate some meat and felt better for the food. She lay wide awake until the warmth of the house and sheer weariness put her to sleep.

Up again at the first break of dawn, she quickly realized she was to face a bad day. The drift beat into her face as she took her sleeping bag out to the sled. Knocking down the snow blocks of her house, she got ready for the day's trip. The dogs shook themselves and came, yawning and stretching, to be harnessed. She hoped the storm would not get worse.

It did get worse. The wind increased as the day passed. She made good headway, but the snowdrifts made it difficult for her to see. She feared that in the storm she might not see Jamieson's place and would go on past it. When night came she knew she must stop. Her clothes were wet with melting snow. If they froze on her she would perish. She must keep moving. She could not put up a house in this storm.

Once, in the shelter of a hill, she stopped the team and melted the ice from the dogs' frosted faces. Then she beat the snow from her clothes and ate a little frozen deer meat. She gave each dog a piece of the meat until it was all gone.

The storm became a blizzard, but she hurried the dogs on. She was grateful that the darkness was relieved by the glow of the unseen Northern Lights. Although not visible, their yellow light filtered through the thickness of the storm. Alea sometimes sheltered her face with her arms. The biting ice cut her skin and she saw blood on her mittens when she wiped the snow from her face.

She drove her team all through the night. She did not know how far it might be to Jamieson's camp. She could see nothing around her for the drift. Often she stumbled over rough ice concealed in the softness of the fresh snow. She held to the lashing of the sled to keep from getting separated from the team.

It was not yet daylight when, with a sudden tug forward, the dogs pulled to a stop. There were answering yelps from nearby, and the glow of light from a window as her team pulled her toward a house. The relief of coming out of the storm to shelter was so great that Alea nearly fell forward.

Jamieson came to the door and his wife followed close behind. Beside a loaded sled he saw a figure he could not recognize in the darkness.

"Come in! Come in, whoever you are," called the genial Scotsman. When Alea remained motionless, the Scotsman hurried out to his unexpected visitor. When he recognized Alea his astonishment held him speechless.

Jamieson told his wife, who had followed him outdoors, "It's the lass from up the bay. What are you doing out in this storm, lass?" Alea tried to speak, but no sound came from her cracked lips.

Mrs. Jamieson was all indignation that Alea should be out in this weather alone. "I knew this would happen to her, and her with no woman to care for her," she exclaimed. "I told you she'd not get well. She's nearly dead from the cold, that's what she is."

But Jamieson knew Ahpea too well to be satisfied that it was just the cold that was wrong here. Putting his hand on Alea's arm, he looked at her closely. "Where's your father, lass? Didn't he come with you?"

As she made a gesture toward the sled, he said to his wife, "Take the girl inside. There's trouble here. Ahpea is not a mon to send this lass out by herself."

Alea again made a motion toward the load and said, in a tone so low that Jamieson just barely heard her, "I brought Atata to you." She could scarcely stand.

Jamieson's face was grave as he asked, "Is that your father on the sled?"

She nodded and he said to his wife, "There's bad trouble here."

Mrs. Jamieson led her to the house. Alea knew her mission was accomplished. Her father was with his friend and Jamieson would know what to do. She let Mrs. Jamieson remove her frosted clothes and put her to bed. She drank the hot partridge broth Mrs. Jamieson brought her. No words were spoken other than Mrs. Jamieson's tender whispering.

"The poor lass is nearly dead with the cold, and to think of her out in that blizzard all alone."

Later Alea heard Jamieson enter the house—heard the subdued voices—Mrs. Jamieson's exclamations of sorrow. Then the door opened and closed again. She knew Jamieson would care for her father and her team. She could leave it all with him now—what her father would have wanted her to do was done.

Next day, in a sheltered place high up on the hillside, Jamieson laid his friend. The wind sent the snow drifting over the newly-turned earth, while overhead the Aurora Borealis gave forth its shafts of light to play soft shadows on its whiteness.

Jamieson stood, a tall figure with rugged uplifted face as the wind blew the snow into his gray hair. He paid silent tribute to Ahpea, who had come to him in his extremity. The moisture in Jamieson's eyes was not due to the cold as he walked down the mountainside. He had said a last farewell to his friend.

20

LIFE WITH THE JAMIESONS

JAMIESON WENT to Aiviktok Post to take the news of Ahpea's death. There was little he could tell, for Alea was very ill and they had not been able to question her.

The trader, Mr. Wilson, was shocked at the news and asked, "What happened to him? He was a fine man, and a good trapper and hunter. I'm more than sorry to hear he is gone. What will happen to the girl? With her father and mother dead and her brother away, she's pretty much alone."

"Aye," replied Jamieson. "She's had a bad shock and is in a pretty bad way herself. She will bide with us. The wife is fond of her. She's a good lass. Made that long trip alone to bring her father to us. Aye, we'll care for her."

"That's mighty kind of you, Jamieson, but that may not be necessary. The girl has distant relatives. Her mother's people will probably be after her to live with them when they get the news."

Jamieson took his pipe from his mouth. His bushy brows lowered as he said heatedly, "The lass came to me and there she will stay unless she herself wants to go away. She's not to be bothered with relatives she never lived with before. She's all right where she is now."

The trader put his hand on the other man's shoulder. "You're a good man, Jamieson, and she's a fortunate girl to have you and your wife to care for her. Come to the store and we'll see about a bit more food. You will need more now with another mouth to feed."

"You need not worry about the food for the lass. She's eaten hardly enough to keep a bird alive. Just sits there looking out as if she were seeing it all again, with never a word 'til we speak to her." Nevertheless, Jamieson returned home with additional food from the kindly trader.

The news spread from person to person and the trader's prediction of people's concern was verified by arrivals at Jamieson's house. There was genuine grief for the passing of Ahpea. Any of them would have given Alea a home, but Jamieson kindly but firmly made it known her home was there and there she stayed. When a cousin of Soona's came one day with his fat wife, all ready to pack up the girl and take her back with them, Mrs. Jamieson could contain herself no longer. One look at Alea's distressed face set her tongue loose.

"And why must she go with you? She never said for you to come after her, did she? She is fine, right where she is. Just leave her be."

Mrs. Jamieson looked so belligerent standing there, with her hands on her wide hips, that her husband laughed and chided her with, "Hoot, woman. Away with your sharp tongue. The lass remains here. There's a good roof over this house and she stays under it as long as she wishes." Then he changed the conversation to a safer subject and when the people left, they felt they had had a nice visit and were glad to know their cousin's daughter was being so well cared for.

A week later Yorgke came with his father to express sorrow and ask if there was any way they could be of service. Jamieson liked this family. They were industrious, hard-working people. But both he and his wife were surprised that Yorgke was not in the armed forces as were Koopah and the other young men of Labrador. When the trapper asked why it was that Yorgke was not wearing a uniform, the young man took Jamieson aside and spoke to him in low tones.

Returning, Jamieson said, "Yorgke has been of valuable help to our country in London as an interpreter. Now he has come back on a secret mission, of which he may not tell." All understood, and no more questions were asked.

As the day was getting late, Jamieson invited Yorgke and his father to stay the night in his house, which they were glad to do. Alea did not join in the pleasant conversation that then ensued, but sat listlessly doing nothing, although some sewing was in her lap. She was not listening to the others. She was busy with thoughts of her own. Yorgke glanced her way several times but did not speak to her.

Mrs. Jamieson, seeing his eyes go to Alea again and again, said, "She's been like that ever since she came. She talks to nobody—never cries—just sits all shut up inside."

After the evening meal Yorgke went over and stood beside Alea as she stood looking out the window into the blackness of the night.

"It's a cold night, but there is no wind," he said.

The girl continued looking out and made no answer. It was almost as if she had not heard him.

"Would you like to go out there?" he asked gently.

To his surprise, she nodded and he said, "Dress warmly," and waited while she got her deerskin coat.

Mrs. Jamieson cautioned, "Don't go too far, Yorgke. It's real cold."

Yorgke let Alea lead the way. He felt a deep pity for this girl whose sorrow had so bowed her down; and as she trudged on, he followed close behind. Up the mountainside she went to stand beside the grave of her father. Together, they stood looking at the mound of earth. Yorgke did not know what to say, but he was convinced Alea's deep grief must not continue. She should not shut herself up as she had been doing.

The night was clear. The sky was covered with stars. The Northern Lights shimmered in majestic glory. Yorgke found it difficult to speak as he looked at Alea's slight form standing there so motionless while she gazed at her father's grave.

"Alea, your father is not where you are looking," Yorgke at last said softly. "He is out there in that light. He is part of all that life out there."

Alea raised her head and looked at the brightness above, but she made no answer. Yorgke continued, "Could all that out there be bright and shining if people we loved were in the ground? I never feel that way. I think it is bright out there because it is full of good people who lived with us once. When they were finished here they went to live in the brightness. They became a part of all the great outdoors."

At his words, Alea sobbed, "He died alone. I was gone and if he wanted something I was not there to give it to him. He died all alone."

"Alea, your father was proud of you. And he knew you would always obey him. If he had wanted you to stay home, he would have asked you not to go. You must stop thinking that way. Do as he would want you to do now. He was happy only when you were happy. He could not stand it if you were sad. I think he sees us now from out there and he says, 'Be happy and take care of yourself . . .' "

She interrupted with a cry. "Yes, that is what he told me that morning. He said, 'My daughter, take care of yourself.' "

Yorgke put his hand under Alea's chin and, turning her face upward, said, "Will you tell me about it? What happened to him?"

"Atata fell over a cliff and hurt himself. I did not know he was so ill, so I left him alone." Yorgke listened while she sobbed out her story. He felt his throat tighten when he heard about her trip in the storm with her father's body on the sled.

When at last Alea fell silent, Yorgke said, "Let us go down now."

Alea fell in step with him. The tears lay cold on her face. Softly Yorgke whispered, "Do you remember the story you told that night at the party about Koopah's Big Star Hunter? I often think of it. That must be Big Star Hunter up there now. Look up, Alea. It is twinkling in brightness."

Suddenly a shooting star streaked across the sky; then it was gone.

"See," said Yorgke, "even the stars lose some of their people, but those left go on shining as brightly as ever."

At the house Mrs. Jamieson was waiting up for them. "Go to bed now and get warm," she told Alea. "Yorgke, I fixed your and your father's bed here by the stove. You'll be comfortable there."

Before going to her room, she went in to see Alea. The girl put out her hand and touched Mrs. Jamieson's face in the dark, saying, "I'm all right now. The sky was so full of stars it was running over. One fell out, but the others went on shining just the same. Atata is out in the light, not down in that cold ground. From now on I'll be as he would want me to be. He said, 'Be careful.' I will, just as he said."

"Bless you, wee one," said Mrs. Jamieson. "There's a lot of good light up there and a lot of it here too, if we look for it. I'm glad you are all right now. My lass, go to sleep."

The following day Yorgke and his father went up the bay to get Alea's skins and other belongings and bring them back to Jamieson's. They feared the wolves might get in and destroy them. All the other things at the little house would be safe until Koopah returned. As they rode along, Yorgke recounted Alea's sad story of Ahpea's accident.

The older man said thoughtfully, "He must have died in his sleep. He brought the girl up like a man or she would never have thought of bringing him out and finding her way to Jamieson's place."

When they returned, the skins were put away for safe-keeping until next summer and the time for the trip to Aiviktok for the annual trading.

With great determination Alea now entered into the life about her. She hauled ice to melt for drinking, set out traps and hunted just as she was used to doing. She helped get meat for the dogs—Jamieson's team as well as her own—of which now they had too many. The dogs ate a great deal of food, so she hunted tirelessly.

Although Mrs. Jamieson was quite aware that this had always been Alea's way of life, she often protested with upraised hands. "You should not be going out today. It's a blizzard out there—no place for a woman!"

With a merry laugh and a hug with arms that never reached around the wide waist of the older woman, Alea dashed out, letting in a blast of cold wind as she opened the door.

One evening, after she returned from her traps, she was mending a broken harness when a sled drove up. Tamanna hustled in, leaving her father outside to care for the dog team.

"Hello, Mrs. Jamieson. Here's some deer sinew my mother sent you. She said that with Alea here now you might be needing more thread to sew with."

"That was right thoughtful of your mother. We can always use sinew," Mrs. Jamieson told her.

Alea looked up at the newcomer, but Tamanna was busy chatting with Mrs. Jamieson, who was asking about people she knew in the part of the country near Tamanna's home. When Jamieson came in with Tamanna's father, they were served food and a cup of good tea.

It was later that Tamanna sauntered over to where Alea was finishing her job. Alea greeted her with a smile but went on working.

Tamanna asked, "You going to live here now?"

"I don't know. I think so 'til Koopah comes."

"Yorgke was here, wasn't he?" she asked with assumed carelessness.

"Yorgke and his father came and many more people." Alea went on working.

Tamanna would not be turned from the real object of her visit. "Do you like Yorgke?" she asked. She had heard that Yorgke had been away from his home longer than just a casual visit to the Jamiesons would take.

Alea looked at Tamanna candidly as she said, "Everyone likes Yorgke. He is a good man like his father."

Tamanna tossed her head. "My mother says you can come and stay with us when the Jamiesons get tired of you, but she said she would not let you dress in men's clothes if you lived at our place!"

Alea's face was angry as she retorted, "I could not walk in that," and she pointed to Tamanna's flouncy dress.

Seeing Alea's stormy face, Mrs. Jamieson said quickly, "If you are done with the harness, lass, you'd better have some of this good partridge you killed today."

There was no more talk between the girls and Mrs.

Jamieson confided to her husband that night, "I heard what that hussy said to the lass and I'd like to tan her bottom—ruffles and all—the stuck-up seal's flipper!"

Tamanna was the last of the winter's callers and life settled back to normal. Alea was loved and surrounded with care and kindness. Out of hopelessness had come comfort once more and a fullness of living that put a song in her heart and a light in her eyes. Life was good again with these friends, whose own lives were fuller for her presence in their home. And surely, surely Koopah would return to her soon.

21

THE BLUE DRESS

SPRING AT LAST ONCE MORE. The tar sizzled as Jamieson ran the hot iron over the seams of his boat in preparation for the trip to the post. Alea waited eagerly to help him launch the boat when it was ready.

Jamieson, always surprised at the work Alea could do, often remarked to his wife, "The lass is as good as any mon. She's handy and strong as an ox."

At this Mrs. Jamieson always threw up her hands in mock despair and said, "She's like a mon all right, in more ways than one. She's not a good cook and she does like to eat!"

When the Jamiesons and Alea arrived at the Post that season, they found many people already on hand. There were Ekoma with her baby, the Perrows and Selalu, smiling and ready to help them land. Indians, Eskimos, halfbreeds—all were there.

As Alea stepped ashore, Selalu was the first to hold her close. "We heard you had great sorrow when our friend Ahpea left us. Our eyes were wet with tears. Selalu could not come to you without dogs. But her love was with you and her wish to help."

Alea nodded. She felt a great sadness at meeting all these friends of her father's whom she had not seen since his death.

The ship was in the harbor. It had only just arrived and many boats were now making their way out to hear the news and visit with the ship's people. Kayaks paddled out across the water, bobbing up and down like corks.

After helping set up the tent, Alea strolled away along the shore to the point where she had often sat with Koopah when they came to the post as children. She saw the ship's smoke trailing across the blue sky and prayed that there would be news of Koopah when the boats returned to the shore. Although the sun was bright, the wind blowing in from the sea made her shiver and she drew her coat closer. Seating herself upon a rock, she watched the waves run up on the shore.

Quick footsteps on the gravel behind her made her turn. It was Koopah holding his arms out to her and with a cry she rushed into them.

"Koopah! Koopah! Don't let me go. Don't go away again. Stay with me!" Even though she clung tightly to him, she could scarcely believe he was real.

"I am home to stay with you, my sister. The war is over."

"Koopah, Atata . . ."

Koopah pressed her to him protectively and said, "I heard, little sister. I saw Yorgke on the ship when he came out. He brought me ashore on his kayak, but when you were not in the Jamiesons' tent I knew you must be here. We will not talk of it now. My sister was brave and might have perished in the great storm that night. I will want you to tell me everything, but not now."

Slowly they walked back to the tent. Alea had not seen Yorgke since she came to Aiviktok. She was glad he had been the one to tell Koopah about their father.

Koopah was reluctant now to talk about Ahpea, for he felt confused. He did not know what was best for him to do for Alea. He wondered whether she would want to go up the bay with him or remain with the Jamiesons. He would have to talk things over with them before he could plan for next winter. He felt a great emptiness at the loss of his father. He had not thought of life without Ahpea. The hurt was deep, and Alea's welfare must be his first thought.

All the young men were welcomed back home joyfully. Everyone rejoiced that the big war was over. People found themselves laughing with a feeling of great happiness that the ship's land was at peace again.

The trappers traded their skins for supplies. New guns were bought and admired; younger boys beamed over long-coveted pocket knives; little children grinned with sticky faces at the trader who did not forget his gift of sweets. After a few days of trading, the people would go back to their hunting quarters. From far and near the boats would be returning home with precious supplies bought with last winter's catch. The hearts of all were high with the hope that next year would be even better.

Then came the last day's stay. Tonight would be the

big dance. Women would wear their best. Men bought new clothes or wore the ones they had kept carefully for this special occasion. All day there was suspense and anticipation. Everyone would be there. All were ready for the big fun.

That evening the accordion was brought out and the dance began early. Koopah had been staying with Yorgke, since there was no room for him in Jamieson's tent. The two young men went to the dance early. Koopah, dressed in his soldier's uniform, was a gay young blade with sparkling eyes and a happy-go-lucky manner.

Still shy, Alea felt no thrill over this grand evening. It was not until the sound of the dancing had been going on for some time that she went in to watch the fun with Mrs. Jamieson. They sat down about halfway up the long room where seats had been placed for the spectators, who were mostly old people or small children.

Koopah sometimes stopped and stood talking with Mrs. Jamieson and Alea. It did not strike him as strange that Alea was not dressed up. To him that was natural. He would have been surprised if she had done so. She was Alea—the most wonderful sister anyone ever had. She would not be happy any way but as she was, and that was the way he liked her. It never occurred to him that she should join in the fun. So, except for a brief stop, he was off again whirling any and all with his usual abandon and grace.

Alea was proud of Koopah in his uniform. There were other young men in uniform, but she thought none was as fine as Koopah.

Mrs. Jamieson was troubled. "It's not right. You should be having fun with them," she said.

Alea laughed and stepped in front of Mrs. Jamieson. Holding her head to one side she patted her trousers and said quizzically, "Go out there like this?"

Mrs. Jamieson smiled but still looked dissatisfied. "You should have worn a dress. You should have dressed up in some of your London clothes and been out there with the others. It's not right for you to just sit here."

It was at this moment that Tamanna and Yorgke came turning by in a slow waltz, and saw Alea in her mannish clothes standing by Mrs. Jamieson.

Tamanna's remark was loud as she giggled, "She should have gone to war with the rest of the boys. She always looks like a man."

There was no answering smile on Yorgke's face. He seemed not to hear her as they danced away across the floor.

Mrs. Jamieson said, "That's a brazen one, that is!"

But Alea did not hear her. She only saw Tamanna's scorn. A pretty dress? She had a pretty dress in her bag—much prettier than Tamanna's flouncy red one!

Taking one more look at Mrs. Jamieson's disturbed face, she said, "Wait here for me. I will show you something." Quickly she slipped along the wall and hurried out into the night toward the tent.

Mrs. Jamieson had never tried to change Alea's way of dressing. She was so anxious that the girl be at ease with them, be well and happy and lead a life that was natural for her, that she had not urged her to wear girls' clothes.

But now she was troubled. She did not like Tamanna's remark, and every time the couple passed by she became angry all over again.

Tamanna was very sure of herself tonight. She was the best-dressed girl at the dance. Her glaring red ruffled dress matched the boldness of its owner. She did not lack for partners but switched from one to another, flirting coquettishly with Yorgke and Koopah, to the disgust of Mrs. Jamieson and the amusement of the others.

Now came a lull in the dancing. The accordion player was out taking a rest, until the caller was heard again. "Take your places. Fill up the floor."

The men selected partners and took positions for the next dance. Yorgke got up from the bench where he had been chatting with Mrs. Jamieson when a figure appeared at the door and paused a moment, blinking in the well-lighted room as she came in out of the darkness. For a time no one moved. All eyes were on the girl in the doorway—a girl in a blue dress with short sleeves and with white lace at the neck and sleeves. Her hair was braided and wound around her head like a crown. She wore black shoes and walked easily as she started for her place by Mrs. Jamieson, who was looking at this vision with incredulous amazement.

Before Alea had crossed the room, Yorgke was beside her. She smiled into his eyes, knowing he had seen her this way before, and delighting in his surprise. Everywhere people were saying, "Is that Alea, the girl from up the bay?" Some asked, "Where did she get the clothes? Is that Alea? You sure?"

Yorgke took her hand and they walked side by side into the crowd. Alea's eyes sparkled like the stars in her pleasure at the surprised smiles and exclamations of her friends. She was happy at the love she saw in their faces.

Yorgke stopped in front of Koopah and Tamanna, who had taken their places and were waiting for the music to start.

"Koopah, this is my friend from up the bay," he said. "The best hunter and trapper in the north."

Koopah forgot Tamanna and all the people. To the delight of all, he hopped about calling his old joyous shout "Hee-ah! Hee-ah!"

Tamanna could not believe this was really happening. For once she was without words. She could only look at this glowing girl who was so transformed she might easily be a stranger. Yet Tamanna knew this was indeed Alea. Where had she gotten that dress? But it wasn't just the dress that had changed Alea, it was Alea herself. Wearing these clothes was giving her confidence and assurance, and she was no longer shy. She was a girl among her own people, enjoying their surprise to the fullest.

Tamanna's face was comical in its dismay, for Alea was certainly the most attractive girl on the floor. Tamanna herself was outshone by this girl who had always been her pattern of what not to be like. She had never regarded Alea as an equal, and the only reason she was concerned about her at all was that Yorgke had always liked Alea, and she did not approve of that. He was the most eligible young man around, and her mother's plans were that she, Tamanna, should be Yorgke's choice when he got ready to choose a wife. Now, here he was doing the honors for this girl who had dumbfounded everyone by appearing in a pretty dress and coming here and making a fool of herself.

Tamanna's lip began to curl. She'd show Yorgke this girl was clumsy and stupid. She had never danced and Tamanna would get Koopah to take her out on the floor. Maybe Alea would get dizzy and fall down and everyone would laugh at her and she'd go back and sit down; then the fun would go on and it would be as it was before.

She gave Koopah a playful push. "Take Alea in the dance," she said. "Let's get started. Yorgke will dance with me."

Alea made a move to go to Mrs. Jamieson, but Yorgke stopped her.

"Will you dance this with me?" he asked.

"I can't. I don't know how. I like to watch," Alea told him.

"We will all help you. Just follow the rest. You'll do it all right. Come."

He led her out and they took their places among the dancers. The music started. The dancers seemed all hands to Alea as she was passed from one to the other in the square dance. But Yorgke guided her at every turn. Her natural love of rhythm made it easy for her to follow his movements, and she was a dash of blue in the crowd in contrast to Tamanna's red, as she wove in and out.

Mrs. Jamieson smiled with pride as she watched Alea. This was as it should be. She was happy to see the lass out there with the other joymakers. Later, when the dancing was over, she saw Alea leave the room with Koopah on one side and Yorgke on the other.

"The lass grew up tonight," Mrs. Jamieson said to her husband. "She has found her place and she'll not be taking any snubbing from the likes of that Tamanna any more." As she spoke she looked at Tamanna, who was leaving with her parents and appeared to be in a very bad mood as she glared at Mrs. Jamieson and went on without a word.

Jamieson grinned as he answered, "The young lad Yorgke seemed to like her anyway."

His wife gave him a quick glance and got up to go. "Shut your mouth, mon." Then she added, "He's a right good lad," and left, feeling that this had been a good night. A wrong had been righted and life would be easier for Alea from now on.

22

THE HAPPY ENDING

When they left the dance, Alea and Koopah and Yorgke went down to the point and seated themselves upon the rocks. Except for the slight swish of the gentle waves against the shore, the night was very still.

Koopah turned with his teasing smile and said, "I'm afraid my sister will be lonely up the bay after looking so fine tonight and . . ."

He got no further, for Alea energetically pushed him, saying, "I'll knock you flat if you say I looked fine!" And she looked about for a suitable club.

Yorgke laughed, then said seriously, "I saw something today I did not understand. I was up here and saw two people sitting over there on the rocks talking. One was a pretty girl and the other my friend Koopah. He talked earnestly and she listened; then she jumped up and ran away toward the tents. But my friend sat here a long time by himself."

If Yorgke expected embarrassment from Koopah, it was not there. Koopah kept on looking out over the sea.

Alea asked in a puzzled voice, "A girl with Koopah? Why did she run away?"

Koopah turned to her and said, "Yes, a nice girl. We talked and she ran away."

"But why?" Alea was ready to be angry if some silly girl had been unkind to Koopah. She could not imagine anyone running away from him.

"Because I asked her to be my wife," Koopah said, so low Alea scarcely heard him.

"Your what?" Alea was so astonished Koopah laughed.

He said gently, "You know Seena. She lives with the Perrows. They did not stay for the big fun. They have already gone to Big River to hunt the muskrat. We sat here and talked, and then she ran away."

"But you just came home. You don't know her," Alea protested, not sure she was hearing him correctly.

Again Koopah very gently answered her, almost as though he were afraid he might hurt her and was on guard against doing so. "I have known Seena a long time. When I was far from home I thought of her often. Even when I was tired and lay in the rain and mud, it was her face that came out of the darkness. When I saw her after I returned, I knew she was the one for me. But when I talked to her about it today, she ran away because she did not want to hurt you, my sister. She felt sure you would not want her up the bay with us."

Yorgke listened but took no part in this conversation.

This was between the brother and sister. As for Alea, she felt bewildered. She had never taken into consideration the fact that some day Koopah would want a wife. She had never thought of sharing him with another woman, but more than anything in the world she wanted him to be happy.

In her confusion, she quite forgot Yorgke and was not aware that he did not take his eyes from her face. He felt heartsick when he saw she was nearly in tears, but she surprised both him and Koopah by asking suddenly, "What was the war like?"

Koopah was ready to talk. "We went to far-off lands. Sometimes we went through mud and rain to help men who were fighting for peace—such peace as we have here tonight."

And so Koopah's story began. For a long time he talked without pause, telling them about Mike, wonderful Mike, who had been his pal in the army and who had been wounded. He smiled as he felt the letter in his pocket that, as Mrs. Jamieson had told him, said Mike was well now and some day would be coming to see Koopah and to "taste some of that seal's flipper, but only a taste." It was Mike who had read Alea's letters to him, Koopah.

"Then the war ended and men were sent home," Koopah concluded, grinning at her. "And when the ship was leaving for Aiviktok, I was among the passengers."

There was silence, with only the waves for sound. Alea knew that whatever she wished, Koopah would do. If she said they should go on up the bay by themselves, he would go without a word of complaint at her decision. But would he be happy? Would she?

She thought of Seena, whom she knew as a quiet girl with a ready smile. She remembered Seena's piquant face with its deep dark eyes. She knew Seena made exquisite clothes with her own hands, and was always neat and attractive. Seena was an Eskimo girl. Her parents had died when she was a child and the trapper Perrow had reared her. He was a good trapper. Now, Seena had run away from Koopah because she wanted Alea to be happy. Was Seena happy now?

Yorgke saw the conflict within her. Then a light that was good to see came over his face as Alea put her arms around Koopah's neck and whispered in his ear. "We want Seena. Go to her and tell her to come back. Go tell her it's all right. It won't make Alea sad for you to take her up the bay."

Koopah jumped down from the rock and looking into his sister's face, said, "When our mother went away she told me to look after you. I could not do that when the great war took me away. You might have died in the storm. I was not there to help you. I want you to be happy, my sister. Seena said we can wait if it is hard for you. I want you to be like you were. You were happy with Atata and Koopah. Now it's only Koopah . . ."

She interrupted him, saying, "The Jamiesons want me to stay with them. . . ."

But Yorgke stepped in front of her to say earnestly, "Long Yorgke has thought of no one but Alea. Ever since the big fun when you stood beside your father and told me your name was Alea, I have belonged to you. Will you let me make you happy? I think I can if you will let me."

Alea stood and looked at Yorgke. She saw the love in his eyes and understood now why it was she had been able to tell her great trouble to him when she could find no words for it with anyone else.

She heard him pleading, "Let Seena make Koopah happy. She is right for him. Alea, come." When he held out his hand, she took it in her own.

Just then the earth was lighted by the play of the Aurora Borealis. It was a glorious sight indeed to the three looking skyward.

"Big Star Hunter never looked brighter nor smiled more happily than he does tonight," Koopah said. Then Alea and Yorgke heard his whisper, "Smile for Seena, too."

As they walked back to the tent hand in hand with Alea between the two men, Yorgke said, "I want to go far to the great north where the good shadows glow the brightest. There must be people out there like us. When the shooting star falls, it streaks toward the north. I want to go there."

Alea felt the surge of adventure stir within her as she looked into his intense face and said, "I will go with you, Yorgke, to the land of the good shadows and the shooting stars."

The moonlight on their faces was no brighter than the

stars in their eyes and the love in their hearts as they walked back toward the tent to face a new life and adventures that tonight reached out inviting arms from an unknown future.